Fluid Structures
Adventures in Engineering

I'm breaking through
I'm bending spoons
I'm keeping flowers in full bloom
I'm looking for answers from the great beyond

R.E.M. *The Great Beyond*

David Crookes

Fluid Structures
Adventures in Engineering

Watermark

This book is dedicated to my wife Pornthida (Earn)
and my beautiful daughter Joy. I love you both.

Frontispiece: Helium balloons, nets, fibreglass rods and
unstable structures – a trial flight of *Sky Ear* by Usman
Haque, the bravest designer I ever met.

Excerpt from *The Great Beyond* – copyright © 1999 by
Michael Stipe, Peter Buck and Mike Mills – reprinted by
permission of Warner Brothers Music. All rights reserved.

Designed and edited by Ian Lambot

First published in Great Britain by Watermark Publications
(UK) Limited, PO Box 92, Haslemere, Surrey GU27 2YQ
www.watermarkpublications.com

British Library Cataloguing-in-Publication Data
A catalogue record for this book is available from the
British Library

Colour Separations by Evergreen Colour Separation
(Scanning) Co Ltd, Hong Kong
Printed by Everbest Printing Company Ltd, Hong Kong
Printed in China

ISBN 978-1-873200-72-8

Contents

Spiral staircase for a private
residence in Stanley Gardens,
designed by Make.

Foreword
by Ken Shuttleworth

When David approached me to write the foreword for *Adventures in Engineering*, I readily accepted. I mean this in the nicest possible way, when I say that Fluid are unusual structural engineers. They do the sort of projects that engineers often don't bother to get involved with – the stair, the footbridge and even the bookcase. As a result, after 10 years, they don't just have the usual portfolio of large 'hairy' projects, rather they have one stuffed with small-scale gems and they seem to have done hundreds of them – many using materials in a particular way for the very first time. All of them are rather beautiful.

Fluid see engineering differently to many other engineers, who simply apply known knowns. They see engineering as a constant search for solutions, an adventure or exploration into the unknown. Their work is a wonderful combination of art and mathematics; it defines the line where art meets science and where the poetic meets the intrinsic properties of materials.

I think the key difference is that individuals at Fluid sketch all the time. They make experimental models to explore the countless possibilities a brief throws up. They pursue solutions through rigorous analysis of a material's properties, yet exercise an aesthetic judgement which make complex forms seem effortless. Fluid take a position in a design team that is not just doing the mathematics but is part artist, part architect and part 'boffin'. The staircase we did together surpasses any I have ever been involved with. It is sublime, uses advanced manufacturing technology and is a joy to behold and to use.

Yet, strangely they don't see themselves as innovators but rather use a process of exploration and experimentation to generate ideas through the materials themselves. They believe this is the way forward, rather than offering off-the-wall suggestions without research. They are process-driven rather than solution-focused; they are fascinated by the journey rather than jumping straight to the end. They make the impossible seem easy, the difficult look refined and the finite seem infinite. This book is a testament to exploration and an inspiration to adventurers everywhere.

Ken Shuttleworth
Founding Partner, Make

London, January 2011

Introduction
by David Crookes

When I was a child I never knew what I would do when I grew up. I talked a lot and I liked making things but I wasn't very gifted at anything. I grew up in Dublin, a wet Irish city where poetry hid in words and people were castigated for pretension. In the end I did engineering and that was really to make my life easier, as I could avail myself of the grant incentives for science students.

We learnt dynamics, statics and soil stability. We studied geotechnics, fluid dynamics and higher mathematics. There was nothing about design and the only time we encountered architects was when they dropped water bombs on us from the top floor during rag week.

When I graduated, I headed to England with my degree and no real understanding of an engineer's work. Sure, I had passed the exams and could do some calculations, but that was it. It took me a while to get a job and I wrote dozens of applications before I was eventually taken on by a small consulting engineering firm with four staff who worked in a Victorian bedroom disguised as an office.

An engineer's drawing office in the 1970s.

It was stuffed full of drawing boards, ashtrays and British Standards, with the floor invisible beneath a carpet of tracing shavings and spent rubber grubbings. The exciting bit was the new Texas calculators (as big as bricks) and inhaling the ammonia fumes from the dyeline machine to numb the boredom of another 100 hand-folded drawing issues. Everything else was routine in a postwar hierarchy where everyone knew their place. The secret of success was to wear a Marks & Spencer suit, buy a new-fangled plastic Samsonite briefcase and learn the Codes of Practice like the star pupil in a structural madrasa.

After two years, I had had enough. I was depressed. My girlfriend left me and I fled to Spain. In Cantabria the sun shone, I taught English to Spanish air hostesses and life was grand. But I was haunted by my failure as an engineer. I contemplated going back to college, but another four years of academia seemed a miserable prospect now I had seen another side of life. Santander was a majestic city, full of beautiful buildings from the Belle Epoque. Their vivacity and playfulness intrigued me, and their details and fairytale facades played with my emotions.

Spending time in the city, it finally began to dawn on me that engineers did not have to be automatons, filled with formulas and numbers; instead, I could become involved in this other world of buildings, art and architecture, of places to visit, live and grow old in. It was my Road to Damascus conversion. I would participate, immerse myself, learn about art and design. It saved me, turned my light green and changed my whole life story.

After that, it was a short step to salvation. I returned to London and found a job at Alan Baxter's in Clerkenwell. He was a big influence on a whole generation of engineers and many of the best had passed through his doors. Although he eyed contemporary architecture with more than a modicum of suspicion, he was in all other ways very much a Modernist and humanist. He employed a librarian and the whole office carried out research into buildings and places. He gathered up the best graduates, black and white, gay and straight, even women! He fed us all three days a week, while we were educated in the broader realm of the engineering profession.

I also started to hang out at architectural crits. I was asked by a great teacher and mentor, James Madge, to become involved at the University of Westminster's School of Architecture. James taught me how to talk to architects, not to be afraid of their vocabulary, and demystified their world. I realised that architecture school was not some special Hogwarts for brewing spells of Minimalism, Deconstructivism or Post-Modernism. I hung around long enough to know that it's not like engineering and that you can't really learn in school how to be a good architect.

As the 1990s came to a close, I set up a practice of my own, Fluid Structural Engineers, and began to build on all the things I had learnt. The idea was to create a technical design house that would operate like an architect's studio, but with architects, designers, sculptors,

Inspirational buildings of the Belle Epoque, including the Santander railway station in Bilbao *(right)* and the Casino in Santander itself *(far right)*.

or anybody from the creative industries who needed technical advice as our clients. We would be 'fluid' in our response and light-footed in our interaction. We did not want the same old working relations that many engineers had fallen into.

A Manifesto for Design Engineers

It is often said that there's very little discussion among engineers about what we do, and that's because we are too busy doing it. It's also true that we do not discuss our work as architects do. There is little in the way of review or recognition among our peers – I don't mean in pure engineering or learned papers terms, but in a broader sense. In terms of creativity, innovation, exploration and so on, engineers generally plough their own furrow and their thoughts and deductions very rarely extend beyond the influence of their own practice.

As this book is about 'Adventures in Engineering', I thought I should set out the issues that allow these two words to sit together without seeming a contradiction. A structural engineer might easily live out his career held in high esteem by his colleagues, if he designs safely and fulfils his professional responsibilities. No one wants buildings to fall down, and if his work guards against this, then who would stone him? His job description could be set down as someone who studies the relevant Codes of Practice and ensures the enforcement of their requirements. In this way he is a model of good practice and a guardian of the knowledge set down by learned committees.

Alternatively, an engineer might take up a position where he or she is open to the concept of testing new ideas and exploring areas of engineering not necessarily set down in the Codes. He or she might pioneer the use of materials, following in the footsteps of Abraham Darby III, the Iron Master, at Ironbridge, or Eugène Freyssinet when he pushed forward the use of prestressed concrete. They might look at an existing material with new eyes and reinterpret

The famous span at Ironbridge, completed by Abraham Darby III in 1781.

FLUID STRUCTURES

its usage, such as Tim Macfarlane's development of glass as a structural material. They might take their inspiration from the world of mathematics, using contemporary computer power to unfold new geometries that would be inconceivable without a mathematical approach.

An engineer coming to the party with these gifts and an open mind is surely the essence of the 'design engineer'. They have a firm belief in the importance of structure as a key ingredient in the determination of a creative act. They recognise that the understanding of forces and their resolution is a fundamental narrative in the development of a design and can only be advanced at any real level of sophistication by their input.

Finally, and in correlation with all these things, engineers working as designers need more than science. They must be willing to worry about how the things they do affect the emotions, and be able to discern what works and what inspires the senses and raises the human spirit. They need more than mathematical skills. They need to read history, understand materials, be ready to draw and spend time in the non-literal world.

Eugène Freyssinet's Pont le Veurdre of 1911, the first prestressed concrete bridge in the world, and his airship hangar at Orly, completed in 1920.

History and Books

It is said that Henry Ford thought that history was bunk. Easily said by a man who limited his Model T to a range of colours that consisted of black, black, black and black. His automobiles were studiously developed and prototyped with exhaustive man-hours well before they rolled off the production line. Most of a structural engineer's work is bespoke and, while the technique of approaching technical issues is consistent, the outcome invariably differs.

Who would want to ignore history in such circumstances? Who would not want to know the reason why the Leaning Tower of Pisa leans, or why Ronan Point partially collapsed, or why the innovative Millennium Bridge, the 'Blade of Light', began to wobble.

Engineers need to be *au fait* with the work of their predecessors and be able to build on knowledge that has been previously accumulated. Most things that an engineer needs to know about concrete shells, for example, he can learn from studying the work of the engineer and

One of Felix Candela's last thin shell concrete structures, the Valencia Oceanogràphic, completed five years after his death in 1997.

structural designer, Felix Candela. He worked mostly in Mexico on everyday projects in concrete and constructed many buildings as tensile shells. Reading about his life and examining photographs of his work is as valuable to an engineer's knowledge as any amount of computer modelling or mathematical non-linear analysis of shells.

Similarly, they can find out about post-tensioned brickwork by reading Bill Curtin's books on reinforced and prestressed masonry and, if they want to start on glass design, they might well begin by reading up on the details and narrative of Tim Macfarlane's early glass work at a residential scale *(see page 43)*. It is impossible for a structural engineer to show a creative hand simply by reading the Codes of Practice or BRE digests. History and books set out where we are, how we got here and offer a vocabulary that is essential for communication between designers.

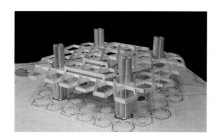

Another Fluid Structures sketch model made out of card and balsa wood.

Materials

We have only really been using steel for just over 100 years; before that, buildings were generally made of masonry and timber. Materials are the lifeblood of engineering and our importance in the great scheme of things (building wise) has been dependent on our ability to make the most of the new ones – to do more with less or offer a new way.

The mechanics of bending stresses, compression blocks, Young's modulus and so on, although very useful, is only a part of understanding materials. You can't design glass beams based on the bending stress of glass if you don't understand the importance of a fail-safe philosophy for the material. You can't create aluminium footbridges without taking account of the material's fatigue criteria and why, mostly, it's better to mechanically fix or glue it rather than weld it. Materials are very hard to learn from standard texts and the best thing a young engineer can do is to build up good relationships with contractors who specialise in a chosen material. There are glass processors in Essex who have built all-glass structures in Japan; aluminium casters in Birmingham who make machine parts for motorbikes; and plastic manufacturers who can fabricate the toughest, lightest and seemingly most impossible free-form shapes.

These special relationships between engineers and material contractors and makers are essential for innovation. They allow engineers to build their real knowledge and find an ally in a time important world, while opening the door for the contractor to broaden the range of work he gets involved in.

Drawing and Making

At engineering school, I learnt to draw with a tee square, whereas nowadays students are educated in the rudiments of AutoCAD. It's all about production drawings, even though they have little use in a design conversation.

Engineers need to pick up pencils and sketch like other designers. They don't need to be brilliant, but they do need to practise and it really should be taught at college. In a way, when an initial drawing is loose and a little vague (even an engineering drawing), it is better as it's open to interpretation, which can be helpful when a design idea is being conveyed. The major stumbling block for engineers who want to be involved in design can often be their lack of skill in developing and conveying an idea. This is magnified by working in a world where designers often stand or fall on their ability to sell an idea to a client as an image.

Sketching is one way of beginning the process of dialogue; another is the making of models and maquettes. This is a process which I have always been interested in and is used extensively in our office. Designers and clients alike love models, and they can often form the focal point of discussions about a project. Engineers' maquettes should never try to be

Fluid Structures make and use models for projects of every scale, including these proposals for shallow, large-span domes in 'thin shell' concrete.

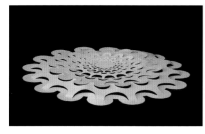

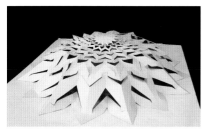

architectural models, as their purposes are completely different. An engineer's model is not a presentation device; rather, it is the three-dimensional exploration of a structural issue. It is also a first run, in miniature, when working out how a bridge or structure might be built, as quite often the same issues occur, irrespective of scale. The model contains information about stability, stiffness, robustness and redundancy, as well as quite often highlighting problems of vibration, dynamics and so on that are not picked up by basic static analysis.

A model starts a dialogue between designers and forms part of the journey. It shows a way and, almost always, opens the door to different and better ways.

What We See

In general, people have a kind of subconscious structural knowledge imprinted in their memories. As they go about their business, they know when something looks right and their eyes tell them, on a daily basis, when something looks a bit slim or heavy-handed compared with the normal

The metre-high precast concrete letters for the portico at Thornton Heath Library.

Among Fluid Structure's more recent projects is the Thornton Heath Library extension with FAT, which opened in July 2010. This included a new entrance pavilion and access ramp constructed in white pre-cast concrete.

A computer rendering of a new educational building by Make, featuring an exposed concrete structure.

Engineering in action – finding a balance between gravity, the tension in the cable and the forces of wind and motion acting on the tightrope walker.

proportions they encounter. This common knowledge is further developed in people involved in making, fabricating or sculpting, but their understanding is very rarely as developed as that of an engineer.

Engineers understand that, while the size of an enterprise may vary, structural solutions are often the same and it is only the scale that changes. The twigs which form a nest, the bones of your diaphragm or the girders and columns of a high-rise building are all the same components in a three-dimensional composition, resolving the forces of bending, tension and compression. Engineers know which materials work best in tension or compression, and when to use a cable or a buttress. They know that you could stack limestone two kilometres high and it probably wouldn't crush. They also know that it's better to be trampled by an elephant than to be stood on by Beth Ditto in killer stiletto heels.

When you look up at a tightrope walker, you see a man on a wire taking his life in his hands. For an engineer, the spectacle is far richer as he really understands the poetry of that tensioned wire, the requirements to maintain gravitational balance and the problems induced by the wind. High-wire acts fascinate us all, but only those who devote their time to structures can really appreciate the performance being played out in the sky.

It is against this background of knowledge that the design engineer weaves his magic. His developed insight into the play of forces is a powerful coda, which can disturb, excite and fascinate. At this moment, in the machismo of the super high-rise tower, in the fragility and amazement of the all-glass structure, in the disturbance of the single column structure, is the potency of the design engineer's hand revealed.

The Book

In this book, I have gathered up various projects that the practice has been involved in since we began. Most of the projects are small in scale and many could be described as domestic. I have separated them into different material sections, so that I could talk a little about the nature of the material and why we chose it for the project.

I have to confess that there's no section on concrete and while, initially, this seemed incredibly embarrassing, I have learned to live with it. The truth is that we have used reinforced concrete on many occasions, mostly for foundations or superstructure frames. However, I don't think we have really had the chance to use the material in an actively new way, and that seems important in a book about adventures.

Concrete has a lot to offer the engineer. It is a material that can be formed and moulded *in situ*. It also precasts pretty well and was fundamental in the emergence of Modernism as an architectural movement. We have started to explore its possibilities and maybe, in 10 years' time, we'll have more to say about it.

Aluminium

Aluminium

I have always been interested in aluminium as a structural material. It seemed so twenty-first century — cool and clean, leaving the dirty old world behind. As a child growing up in the 1960s, it was the embodiment of a future of jet engines and space exploration. It had a thousand faces, from garden furniture to anodised picnic cups, from Airstream trailers to Muji's neat and urban pencil cases.

Years later, a girlfriend bought me Jorge Pensi's Toledo Chair as a birthday present. I just got the one and had to wait six months for Amat to ship it in from Spain. The girlfriend is long gone, but I still have the chair. It's soft to touch, easy to lift and once seen not easily forgotten. It marries a sand-cast seat and back pieces with extruded aluminium legs. It captures the essence of the material wonderfully and the castings carry the echo of a spine and bones, something always alluring to structural engineers.

Aluminium has come a long way in a short time and has kept its reputation as a modern material. Its early home was in the aircraft industry, but it has branched out into many other fields, including electronic hardware and robotics. Honda's walking robot, Asimo, has an aluminium frame and so, most likely, does your mobile phone. The thing is, aluminium can be manipulated and adapted to suit a myriad of functions. It can be drawn, extruded and cast. It can also be alloyed with a host of other materials to increase its strength or formability.

Many times when I saw something that I liked in the world of furniture or product design, it was made of aluminium. These objects ranged from Marc Newson's Lockheed Lounge Chair to Philippe Starck's lemon squeezer, from the aluminium pots and pans neatly piled up in kitchen shops to the six-pack of beer in your hand.

The world has been filling up with aluminium applications, yet in architecture and engineering it didn't seem to be happening. Yes, there are moments such as Buckminster Fuller's geodesic dome in Montreal or Future Systems' beautiful media centre at Lord's Cricket Ground, but mostly it's just cladding or extrusions, never the primary form. I always thought that we could do more with aluminium structurally and whenever a chance arose to recommend the material, we were on it.

Aluminium as a structural material as seen in Jorge Pensi's Toledo Chair.

A Short History

The history of aluminium is a relatively short one, as its existence was only really confirmed in the early part of the nineteenth century. Metallic aluminium does not occur naturally and it was down to chemists to find ways to extract the base metal from the various oxides and silicates it occurs in, most notably bauxite. For many years it was considered more expensive than gold, and in 1884 the tip of the George Washington Monument was crowned with a 2.8-kilogram pyramid of this special metal, the single largest casting then achieved. It was

Sir Alfred Gilbert's statue of Eros in Piccadilly Circus, one of the earliest uses of aluminium in the UK.

used as it was a good lightning conductor and it would not corrode, thus avoiding staining the column's pale stone.

In 1886, Charles Martin Hall — then just 22 years old — in the United States of America and Paul L.T. Héroult in France both perfected an electrolytic method for producing aluminium from aluminium oxide. This, combined with new methods of producing alumina from bauxite ore, resulted in the price of the metal plummeting from $18 a kilo to $4.50. This changed the material from a luxurious precious metal, employed in the manufacture of jewellery, and allowed it to break into a new world of manufacturing and construction.

That said, the new material did not easily find a role in its early years. Many aluminium manufacturing businesses were established between 1885 and 1900, but few survived into the twentieth century. It was never going to be the 'new iron' as many had predicted, but its lightness and benign inertness provided characteristics that could be championed over other metals.

Aluminium as a structural material as seen in the Wellington bomber, first built in 1936 and based on a geodesic structure devised by Barnes Wallis.

The Montreal Biosphère, a near perfect geodesic sphere designed for Expo 67 by Buckminster Fuller.

Despite these early difficulties, the world production of aluminium increased rapidly — from about 200 tonnes in 1905 to in excess of 30 million tonnes by the early part of the twenty-first century. The extraction of the base metal from its ore, however, is not a low embodied energy process. Producing a tonne of aluminium uses about 120 times as much energy compared with a tonne of timber, though it's not as bad with steel, requiring only five times as much!

The saving grace is that there is an energy saving of 95 per cent in production when aluminium is recycled. In the UK, the secondary or recycled aluminium industry exceeds the production of primary metal and, in this way, the metal is promoted by the industry as an 'energy bank'. Aluminium's low melting point of 660°C is far less than that of steel, making a case for recycled aluminium as an acceptable environmental choice. It should be noted that embodied energy is not the only criterion for sustainable design, as you might find that corrosion-free aluminium would also be a better choice for a structure requiring a long lifespan with limited maintenance.

The Properties of Aluminium

Aluminium has a reputation as a wonder material which can be adapted to a thousand outcomes. The reasons for this lie in the diverse range of physical, chemical and mechanical properties enjoyed by the metal and its alloys in either cast or wrought forms, which can be listed as follows:

- it has a very low density, size for size only one-third the weight of steel
- aluminium and most of its alloys are highly resistant to most forms of corrosion, with the metal's natural coating of aluminium oxide providing a barrier to the ravages of air, temperature, moisture and chemical attack

The iconic Airstream caravan *(right)* that first appeared in 1947 and the Future Systems-designed Lord's Media Centre of 1990 *(far right)*.

- it is a superb conductor of electricity – a property, when allied with its other intrinsic qualities, that has ensured its replacement of copper in many situations
- it is non-magnetic and non-combustible, properties invaluable in advanced industries such as electronics or in offshore structures
- it is non-toxic and impervious, qualities that have established its use in the food and packaging industries since the earliest times
- it is ductile and malleable, allowing it to be pulled into thin wires or rolled into sheets. It can also be cast and extruded into complex and bespoke shapes
- it can be coloured by anodising and readily accepts ink printing on its surface
- finally, it can receive many surface treatments, including shot blasting, beading, polishing and waxing.

Cast Aluminium Staircase

The cast aluminium stair was a work of love and a project that I am really proud of. As a practice we did things to make it possible that I would never recommend, but sometimes, just occasionally, the madness takes hold!

Julian Arendt is an architect practising in west London whom we had worked with on several occasions in the past. The relationship is healthy and based on trust; he is a talented designer with strong ideas, but he also lets you put forward your own thoughts. I remember the start of this project when he said that there would be a stair which was central to the project – a special stair that would be the centrepiece of a refurbishment for private clients converting an old school into their home.

At the time I was very interested in using aluminium more as a structural material and was frustrated that it only seemed to show up on buildings as cladding and fenestration. We talked about how we could make a special stair in cast aluminium, how it would have the curves of a polished 1950s' fender, how it would have real three-dimensional qualities and how

A cardboard model of the stair explores the geometry and relationship between the different strings.

it would work beautifully in the context of the space he was creating. The contractor had very different ideas. He said that if the stair were done in stainless steel it would cost approximately £40,000, but if we pursued the aluminium idea then it would be double that.

We weren't very happy about this, and when we cross-examined him as to why this was the case, he said: 'Well, we've never done this before, everyone does stainless and we've never worked with aluminium'. I told the client that this was unreasonable and we hatched a plan to procure the stair in a different way. Fluid would take charge, find the specialist subcontractors and make it all happen. You should never do this!

The cast and polished stair with its hardwood treads and the countersunk socket heads visible on the inside.

CAST ALUMINIUM STAIRCASE

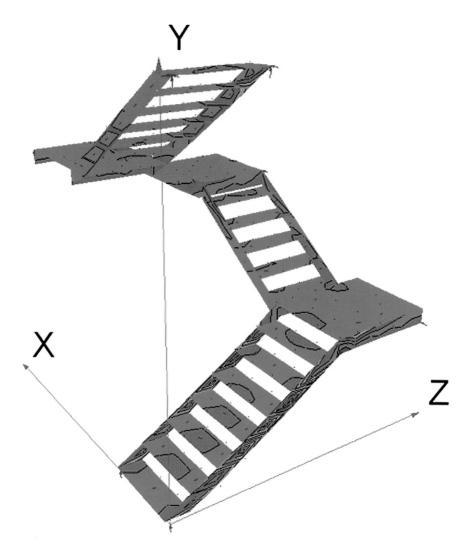

Maximum stresses (kN/m²)

-10620.3
-10000.0
-5000.0
0.0
5000.0
10000.0
15000.0
20000.0
25000.0
28525.7

Y

X

Z

Finite element modelling of the stairs with stresses shown as a coloured topography.

The principal connection was made up in the office with balsa wood and plaster of Paris.

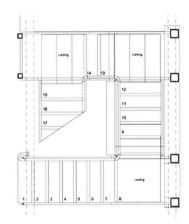

Plan of the staircase
showing all four flights.

After some careful research we found a foundry in Peterborough called Barron-Clark Castings Ltd, which specialised in cast aluminium. They mostly did machine parts or parts for motorcycles, but they were keen to try something new and they undertook to cast the eight strings we needed. The cost of the mould was about £12,000, but with some careful planning and detailing we found we could use the same mould for all eight, which then cost about £1000 each to cast. They were sand cast in aluminium (grade LM6) and even included little lug plates to receive the timber treads, so that brackets would not have to be post-fixed by drilling fixings into the finished casting.

The next step was to find someone to machine the strings so that they fitted together comfortably. This was a very important and delicate job. If they were over machined, you could not simply weld a piece back on – it had to be perfect. The connection would consist of three countersunk threaded bolts fitting snugly into the fat of the casting, which were drilled to receive helicoil inserts.

The connection between
the strings was explored
with physical models.

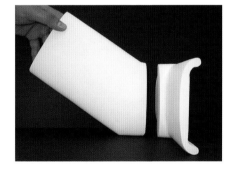 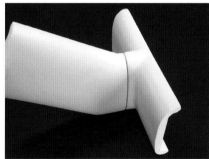

For this job we approached Mark Winder of Silverfern Fabrication. Mark is an unflappable Kiwi ex-oil rig worker who runs a steel fabrication shop in Fulham. But he's more than that: he understands quality, relishes a challenge and employs some fantastic Kiwis and Aussies who are doing their two-year around-the-world stint in the UK. Mark did the machining work (although rumour has it that he got it done by some Indian craftsmen in Southall) and we paid him £7000 for his work and the erection of the stair.

Finally, the issue of the finish needed to be addressed. I was very keen on 'glass beading' the aluminium, which produces a softer and more tactile finish than shot blasting. I also felt that it was more compatible with the sand-casting technique, which usually results in some small grain inclusions being noticeable on the surface. Julian, however, wanted to polish the stair and argued that it was more true to the original concept. He felt the finish was

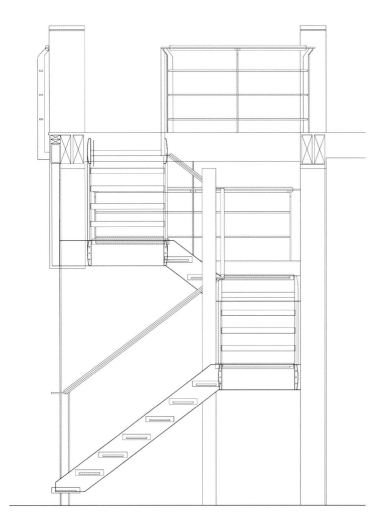

The connection details were hand drawn for discussion with the architect and casting company.

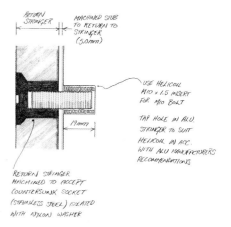

Elevation of the staircase showing the four pairs of strings between ground and first floors.

The strings were 'fattened' at the connection to accommodate the bolting mechanism.

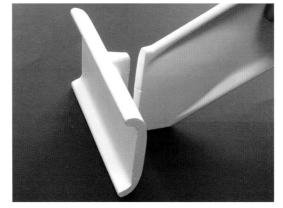

A drawing by Julian Arendt Associates showing the setting out dimensions for the strings.

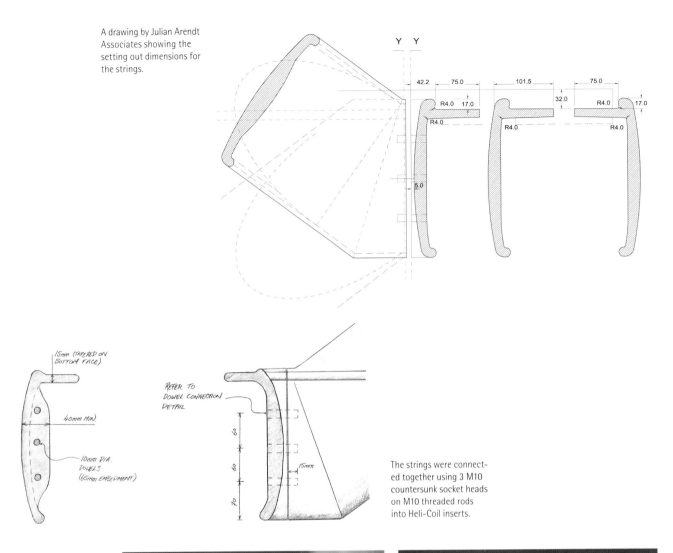

The strings were connected together using 3 M10 countersunk socket heads on M10 threaded rods into Heli-Coil inserts.

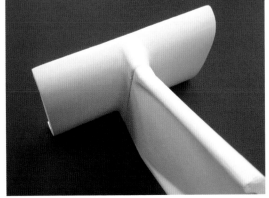

The 'fat' in the balsa wood model was made up in plaster of Paris and sanded by hand.

analogous to pewter and that any slight imperfections were not a thing to worry about, rather something to relish. In the end he was right. We found the best polishers in the UK and the work was done at £100 per metre run, for a total cost of £3000. They were nervous about the curved profile, but the finished pieces turned out really well.

There's something else I should tell you about this stair: the problem we had with the connections. When we prepared the structural drawings for the casting company, they could not understand what we wanted to do at the string-to-string connection. We said that we would send them a three-dimensional digital file, showing them how it should look, but they just laughed and said that it wouldn't make any sense to them.

They wanted British Imperial Engineering drawings like the ones you used to see for setting out machine parts. We kind of knew what they meant, but no one in the office was old enough to remember how to do such a thing. In the end, we made the connection out of balsa wood and plaster of Paris. Ahmet Ucakan, a young graduate working for us at the time, stayed

The staircase was trial assembled offsite to test it for fit and stability.

A cast aluminium string weighs one third of its steel equivalent and was easily manhandled.

in the office until two in the morning, sanding the belly of the connection until we were happy that it was 'sexy' enough. You always need good people in the office who can make stuff and he was one of the best we ever employed.

I learnt a lot from that inability to communicate. The balsa and plaster model that we made and couriered to them was perfect for their purposes, but it set us thinking. Nowadays we would draw the connection using Rhino software and then have it rapid prototyped – maybe in Hong Kong or China where such work is very cheap. They would make it at one-to-one scale and then courier it back to us within 48 hours, which would avoid all the sanding and gluing business. Still, the point is that sometimes making is the most important part of an engineer's toolbox and you just have to step back and be practical.

Section through a pair of strings showing lug plates that support the treads.

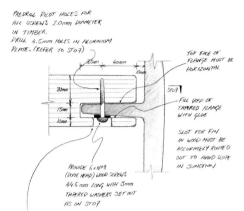

PREDRILL PILOT HOLES FOR
ALL SCREWS 2.0mm DIAMETER
IN TIMBER.
DRILL 4.5mm HOLES IN ALUMINIUM
PLATE. (REFER TO ST07)

75mm 40mm 10mm

33mm

15mm
10mm

TOP FACE OF
FLANGE MUST BE
HORIZONTAL

ST07

FILL VOID OF
TAPERED FLANGE
WITH GLUE

SLOT FOR FIN
IN WOOD MUST BE
ACCURATELY ROUTE'D
OUT TO AVOID SLOPE
IN JUNCTION

PROVIDE 6 x N°8
(DOME HEAD) WOOD SCREWS
44.5mm LONG WITH 3mm
TAPERED WASHERS SET OUT
AS ON ST07

PROVIDE PLUGS FOR
EACH SCREW ONCE
FIXED IN ACCORDANCE
WITH ARCHITECTS DETAILS

Connection detail showing fixing of timber tread to a string with hidden screws.

Trial erection of the aluminium strings prior to sending them out for polishing.

The first strings of the
stair are supported on
tensioned rods which
allow them to 'hover'
above the floor.

The cast and polished
aluminium strings have
a unique language and
aesthetic quite different
from that of stainless
steel.

CAST ALUMINIUM STAIRCASE

Science Museum Energy Ring

The Energy Ring at the Science Museum is 13 metres in diameter and hangs in the main atrium space of the East Hall. The idea for the ring came from the designer Roger Mann of Casson Mann and it was designed as an attraction that would draw people up to the second floor where a new Energy Gallery had been created. The ring has LED strips on the inner circumference and a stabilising horizontal arm which extends at the top. Messages and graphics flashed up on the LED display scroll around and draw the reader's eye up to the floors above.

When we first became involved, the challenge of installing a large ring in the space seemed onerous. The ground floor is littered with precious components of Britain's heritage, engines and machines dating back to the birth of the Industrial Revolution, many of which are priceless historical artefacts. Moreover, the project managers made it abundantly clear that should anything be damaged, there was not enough professional indemnity cover in the world to protect us as structural engineers.

The project quickly evolved into the resolution of two fundamental issues: what was the ring to be made of and how could we install it in such a precious and confined space? Our

The central atrium of the Science Museum is filled with priceless artefacts of Britain's industrial heritage.

The aluminium ring at the Science Museum is made up of 16 segments bolted together and suspended from the existing roof structure.

The main facade of the Science Museum overlooking Exhibition Road.

inclination was to make the ring using cast aluminium sections. We could make a mould and then use this to cast as many segments of the ring as would be necessary. Aluminium was the preferred material as the ring was to hang from the existing roof of the Science Museum and we were not certain of its capacity to carry additional load. With a weight one-third that of steel, aluminium seemed an obvious choice, that was also fully in the spirit of a museum filled with suspended aircraft and rocket engines.

The second issue was how to assemble the ring as quickly and safely as possible. For this, it was proposed to assemble the segments in mid-air on a raisable jig. The topmost sections would be connected first, after which the jig would be raised to allow further segments to be added. Drawing on one of the material's best assets, its lightness, the aluminium segments could easily be manipulated by hand.

At tender stage, it became apparent that aluminium laser cut from flat sheets before being welded together was likely to be a more economical solution than casting, with the

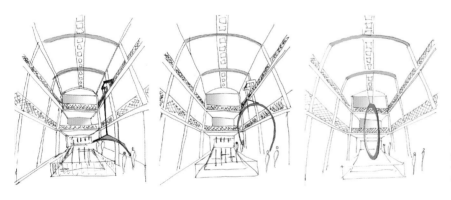

A very important part of our role was determining how the ring could be assembled in the space while minimising the risk to the Museum's exhibits.

added benefit that it would be easier to create a strong but hidden connection between the segments. For ease of handling, the ring was designed as 16 segments, each of which took the form of a deep curved channel formed in 6mm-thick aluminium sheet, with closing plates at each end. Individual sections would then be connected using two bolts which would draw the end plates together. Once the ring was complete, the bolts were torqued up and a cover section laid into the channel to hide the connections and offer a continuous bed to support the 32,000 white LEDs and their wiring.

A trial assembly of the ring was specified to examine the fit of the sections and to make sure the whole thing could be assembled easily once the lifting jig was erected. This was carried out in the manufacturer's car park and satisfied all the structural requirements.

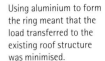

Maximum stresses (kN/m²)

-714.8
-600.0
-400.0
-200.0
0.0
200.0
400.0
600.0
800.0
1000.0
1200.0
1400.0
1600.0
1800.0
2000.0
2200.0
2400.0
2600.0
2743.1

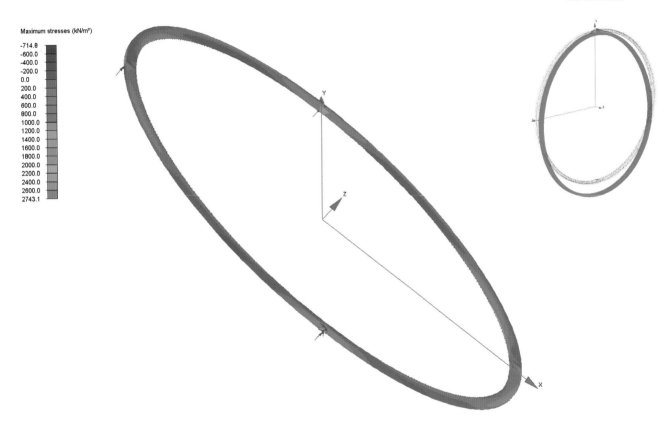

The ring was analysed to check that its deformation when suspended would not be excessive.

However, it did show up small areas of misalignment in the end-plate connections, and it was therefore decided to finish the material by electric wire brushing. The benefit of this was twofold: enthusiastic wire brushing would even out the small misalignments and help the sections to line up, while also forming a continuous texture on the relatively soft aluminium that would take the eye away from the component parts. Rather than a set of individual parts, the continuity of the ring as a single element was thus emphasised, and a good base was also formed for the finishing coat when it was finally selected.

The installation was carried out by Specialist Rigging, a niche-market contractor that makes a respectable living hanging and installing unusual artefacts at exhibition and art venues. The work went well and the whole ring was assembled over a single weekend, with the

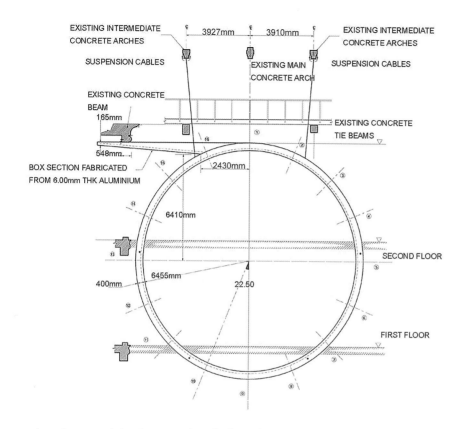

EXISTING INTERMEDIATE CONCRETE ARCHES

3927mm   3910mm

EXISTING INTERMEDIATE CONCRETE ARCHES

SUSPENSION CABLES

EXISTING MAIN CONCRETE ARCH

SUSPENSION CABLES

EXISTING CONCRETE BEAM
165mm

EXISTING CONCRETE TIE BEAMS

548mm

BOX SECTION FABRICATED FROM 6.00mm THK ALUMINIUM

2430mm

6410mm

SECOND FLOOR

400mm

6455mm

22.50

FIRST FLOOR

only real concern being the protection of other exhibits nearby as first the jig and then the individul elements of the ring were lifted into place. Once complete, the ring was carefully manoeuvred into its final resting place, after which stainless-steel tie rods were fitted that allow the ring to be suspended from the curved arches that support the roof above. Finally, a horizontal 'arm' from the top of the ring was tied back to the adjacent floor slab to provide lateral support.

The issue of specifying the aluminium finish was an interesting one which occurred quite late in the day. Consideration was given by the design team to a number of options. As engineers, however, we thought it important to ensure that the material itself, the aluminium, was not obscured or denied by the finish. Anodising was considered, as was shot blasting, glass beading and so on, but in the end it was decided to simply wax the aluminium after its wire brushing to inhibit oxidation. This enriched the metallic lustre and was suitable because the ring is suspended out of the way of children's sticky hands!

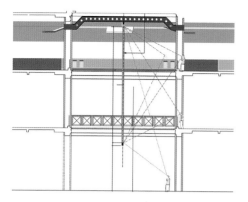

Side elevation of the ring showing its position within the atrium.

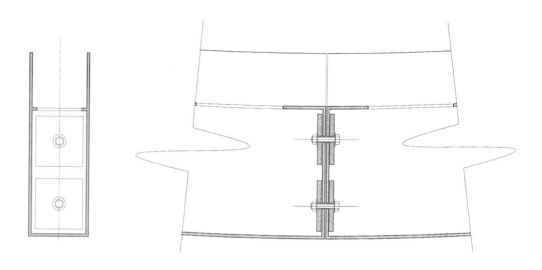

The sections of the ring were bolted together by aligning their end plates and securing them with two bolts and square washers.

A trial assembly was carried out in the fabricator's car park to check that the sections aligned and to allow it to be wire brushed.

The completed aluminium ring with its LED lighting fitted, guiding visitors to the new Energy Gallery on the second floor.

The ring during erection. The basic work was done over a weekend, with the sections assembled sequentially on a jig that could be raised as work proceeded.

Glass

Glass

As an engineer I wasn't really aware of the possibilities of using glass as a structural material early on in my career. I remember seeing the glass extension that architect Rick Mather had designed with the engineer Tim Macfarlane and being absolutely astonished by what they had achieved. The project was a small extension to a house in north London and all the structural components were glass, including the beams, columns/fins and the double-glazed units.

That project was a powerful revelation and I set out to learn as much as possible about the material and its structural possibilities. I think Tim tells a story about trying to get technical information from Pilkington in the early days and they were very reluctant to share what they knew. In fact, he only really got to grips with basic bending stresses by back calculating from the loads and glass thicknesses that were recommended by the various suppliers at the time.

As young engineers we were amazed that a transparent material could be used structurally in buildings. Our surprise was not really based on anything other than the prejudice that glass was for windows and bottles, and that these roles were so firmly established that it was difficult to break that mindset. Once we began to look at glass as an engineering material, however, a different mentality took over. We realised that it was a sheet material (like plywood) and could be put together in similar ways to make columns, beams, floors – all the basic components of the structural lexicon. Obviously the material has its own particularities and these need to be taken into consideration when used for primary elements. Also, because of the potential for instantaneous failure, structural glass always needs to be used with a fail-safe mechanism in place.

Our first projects came long after we had started to gather information and collect pictures, articles and books. I walked Regent Street and Oxford Street, looking at glass facades to see the sizes, how they were stabilised and trying to discover whether the glass was toughened or float. In those days, shop windows were mostly (annealed) float.

The first glass job I ever did was a single-storey staircase in west London with the architect Keith Tillman. Keith and I had been teaching together at the University of Westminster and he won a commission to refurbish a two-storey apartment for a mother and her young daughter. Keith's penchant was for architectural minimalism with lots of white walls, natural finishes and copious hidden storage. He told me about the stair and its importance in the scheme. It would connect the floors, allow light to drop down the stairwell and provide a space below the half landing in which the client could sit and read in peace. Most importantly, the stair should be glass – not partly glass, but all glass!

I took it on and promised him it would be fine and that he was in very capable hands. Needless to say that I regretted agreeing to this many times during the design and construction and can honestly say I woke up several times in the middle of the night as I tried to build it in

An early Fluid Structures design for a clear glass mezzanine floor in a private library.

The staircase for Keith Tillman with its clear glass string and sand-blasted glass treads, both taped onto clear acrylic as a fail-safe.

Where possible, the treads for the Tillman staircase are securely set into grooves in the adjacent walls.

Designed in collaboration with architects Urban Salon, this new Oliver Sweeney shopfront eschews glass fins and mechanical fixings to allow clear views deep into the store.

Wind loading resistance is provided by randomly spaced, white-painted steel tubes.

The classic 'butterfly' crack pattern of a nickel sulphide failure.

my dreams. In the end, though, it was built successfully and it's fair to say that everybody loved it. The treads consisted of float glass on an acrylic fail-safe layer. There was also a glass beam which picked up four or five treads at half landing level above the client's reading space. The glass contractor Malcolm Armfield made me walk up it first as there was still a small sense of bewilderment that such a thing could work!

As a practice, we have moved on over the years to engineer a lot of schemes using glass as the primary structural element. Each project has built up our knowledge about a material that can only really be engineered by taking due account of the technical processes involved in its making and fabrication.

Structural calculations and analysis are a small part of the engineer's armoury when working with the material. Equally he/she needs to know which type of glass to specify, how it should be laminated, what sizes can be toughened, what thicknesses can be heat strengthened? In truth our knowledge of glass has built up over nearly two decades and in that time the glass industry has revolutionised in terms of both the sizes of toughened sheets available and the range of products coming to market. We have also finally learnt to tell the difference between a real nickel sulphide failure or clumsy installations, the difference between a thermal shock fracture and kiddies throwing stones.

A Few Words on the Making of Glass

There's an old story that Phoenician sailors, circa 1000 BC, were camping on a beach one night. They put their cooking pots on blocks of natron (soda), which was the cargo they were carrying in their hold. In the morning they found that the heat of the fire had fused the sand and soda together to make glass.

In Michael Wigginton's book *Glass in Architecture*, he tells of an Assyrian recipe from about 650 BC for making glass, which was made up of:

60 parts sand
130 parts salicornia (soda)
5 parts saltpetre
and 2 parts lime.

Salicornia is a plant group containing soda which can be found growing around coastal areas. When burnt, its ashes can be used as part of the glass recipe. Lime is obtained from grinding down seashells, while saltpetre (potassium nitrate) can be obtained by draining off dung heaps and blending the nitrates with potash (wood ash).

A brief timeline outlining the key moments in the evolution of man-made glass from 5000 BC to the present day.

5000 BC	first recorded use of glass
3500 BC	glass beads in Egypt
1600 BC	glass vases in Mesopotamia
1500 BC	glass jars in Egypt
650 BC	first glass-making manual
27 BC	glass blowing discovered
AD 100	Roman use of architectural glass; creation of the Portland Vase
C11th	sheet glass skills develop
C12th	Venice, glass capital of the world
1674	lead crystal discovered
1860s	industrialisation of glass making
1905	modern flat glass perfected
1959	Pilkington's float process

The Guardian Visitors' Centre Bookcases

In 2001 I was asked to give a lunchtime talk about the work we were doing in glass at Conran & Partners' office in Shad Thames. Unbeknown to me, the girlfriend of one of the partners at another practice, Allies and Morrison, was in the audience and heard the talk. A few weeks later I got a phone call asking if I would go and visit them to discuss a project they had been working on for The Guardian Visitors' Centre in Farringdon.

When we arrived at Allies and Morrison's office, it quickly became apparent that we were not wanted as engineers for the whole project, but simply to give them a hand with a couple of bookcases that they wanted to install in the main display area of the refurbished building. Hiding our dismay we agreed that we would be delighted and that, yes, 'it would be no problem.' Little did we know, though, that the bookcases were to be made of glass, stand almost six metres tall and be used to retain leather-bound copies of historic editions of *The Manchester Guardian*. When I saw the books I nearly cried; they were enormous and each must have weighed in excess of 15 kilograms. Having committed to the project and having

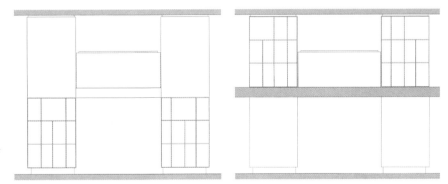

Front and rear elevations of the bookcases, with the lower shelves facing into the main space while the upper shelves face towards the mezzanine.

confidently asserted – yet again – that it would be no problem, we were now stuck with making it work or being mortified with embarrassment.

The bookcases stand at the far end of a double-height display area, on either side of a central opening and concealing a small mezzanine. Fabricated entirely in glass, each bookcase is, in fact, made up of two sections — a bookcase at ground level facing into the display area and a second, above this, facing towards the mezzanine — but with the two sections then dressed to give the appearance of a single tall unit.

Unsurprisingly, the bookcases had to be designed with redundancy, so that if one element fails the whole system does not become unstable and dangerous. To this end the shelves were designed to span between glass dividers at approximately 900mm centres. If the

A completed bookcase with its shelves full of leather-bound books. The discreet mechanical restraints can be seen on the top edge.

divider fails, then the shelf can, in the short term, span double the distance with increased deflection but with enough strength not to break. If a shelf breaks, then the massive books can drop down onto the shelf below which has been designed to take the increased weight. Finally, the back of the bookcase consists of two sheets of 8mm toughened glass, laminated together, so that if one sheet fractures, the second acts as the redundant element. This back piece is very important as it provides lateral strength – like a shear wall – to the whole assembly.

The other key issue was that, for aesthetic reasons, the whole system should be glued together with no mechanical fixings. As a practice we had seen similar pieces of furniture made this way for shop fit-outs and so on, but not at this scale. Quite often the glass was UV bonded together, but we were very wary of this technique. Sometimes, with UV bonding, the joint can be very stiff, such that if one of the glass pieces fractures – because of impact, nickel sulphide failure or the like – the shockwave travels across the joint and breaks the next piece and so on. This was not going to be an acceptable risk for these bookcases. We chose instead,

therefore, to glue the glass elements together using a more flexible black structural silicone. This was carried out in the factory, with thinner joint thicknesses from those normally used in the facade industry, and with the silicone set back slightly so that it did not extend fully to the front face. Fundamentally, silicone is a compatible material with glass, which is itself made of silicate. The two of them can combine at a molecular level to affect a very strong bond, provided that the surface preparation is correct.

Calculations were prepared and drawings were forwarded to Islington Building Control many months before manufacture and, as there was no immediate response, we assumed that they were acceptable and proceeded with the work. However, about two months before the installation, Building Control decided that the proposals were not acceptable and that the elements of each bookcase would need to be fixed together mechanically.

The glass bookcases were assembled as four main components in the glazing contractor's factory.

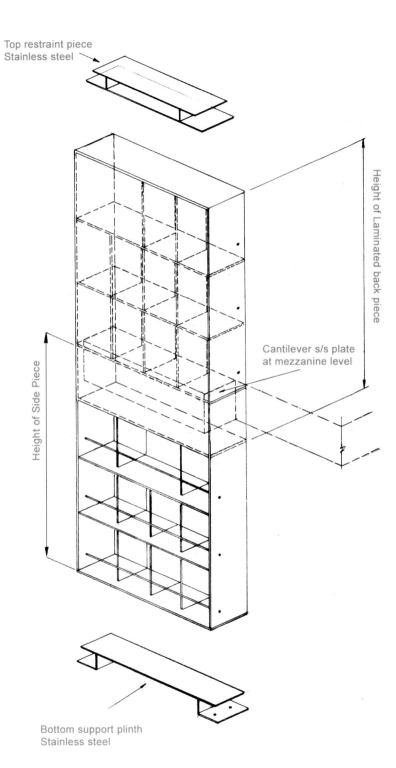

Top restraint piece
Stainless steel

Height of Laminated back piece

Cantilever s/s plate
at mezzanine level

Height of Side Piece

Bottom support plinth
Stainless steel

A hand-drawn view of
the bookcase showing
the relationship with the
concrete mezzanine floor
level.

The completed glass
bookcases were secured
in plywood boxes before
delivery to site.

This was a potentially disastrous blow very late in the day and would alter the physical appearance of the cases tremendously. To appease their concerns, we spoke to Dow Corning – an internationally respected silicone manufacturer – to gather support for our proposals. They were not keen to be involved directly, but they did point out that silicone had been used for many years and in far more onerous conditions than we were advocating. In the USA, for example, silicone has been used to 'glue' facades onto buildings and many of these systems have stood the test of time for 25 years or more.

With this background information and a very decent factor of safety in our calculations, we went to meet the Council officers and, in the end, a compromise was agreed. Now, the only required mechanical fixings were a few brackets and fasteners to restrain the top of the bookcases at head level. These were set back so that they are not immediately apparent, but can be seen peeping out at the top if you look carefully.

Finally, I should comment on the 'whiteness' of the cases. This was achieved by using a ceramic frit on the glass and a white vinyl interlayer between the two sheets that make up the back and sides of the bookcases. I should also point out that the stainless-steel bars are not structural, but are merely to stop people from pilfering the volumes. To tell the truth we did not want them, as they pass through holes in the glass dividers. And we don't like holes as they cause stress concentrations!

The glass cases being assembled on site. Each section was lifted into position using a lifting genie and bolted down before the double-height side pieces were added.

The upper cases sit on the concrete mezzanine slab and are secured by a metal head restraint.

A detail drawing showing how the upper case can be manipulated in terms of level by means of steel shims.

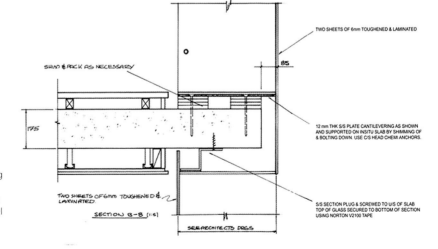

SHIM & PACK AS NECESSARY

175

TWO SHEETS OF 6mm TOUGHENED & LAMINATED.

SECTION B-B (1:5)

SEE ARCHITECTS DRGS

TWO SHEETS OF 6mm TOUGHENED & LAMINATED

85

12 mm THK S/S PLATE CANTILEVERING AS SHOWN AND SUPPORTED ON INSITU SLAB BY SHIMMING OF & BOLTING DOWN. USE C/S HEAD CHEMI ANCHORS.

S/S SECTION PLUG & SCREWED TO U/S OF SLAB TOP OF GLASS SECURED TO BOTTOM OF SECTION USING NORTON V2100 TAPE

View of one of the
bookcases fully loaded
with leather-bound
books.

A close-up view of one
of the bookcases – the
apparent fragility of the
glass heightened by the
massing and density of
the books.

View of the upper book-
cases at mezzanine level,
with some of the security
bars removed.

Clarendon Close Conservatory

The glass arches at Clarendon Close were a labour of love and a source of great consternation in our office at the time of their installation. Andy Martin Associates asked us to act as engineers for the refurbishment of a four-storey Georgian mews house in west London, which was also to include a new single-storey rear extension. For planning reasons the form of the extension had to be similar to the existing, but this time the roof would incorporate clear glass vaults with no visible framing.

Initially, we were very pleased, as the idea of using glass arches was an exciting area to explore, and in the early days the project proceeded as normal. There were walls to be removed, a new staircase to be introduced, works to the basement and alterations at roof level. All of this was relatively straightforward and well within the remit of the office.

When the design for the extension was prepared, we specified that the new double-glazed vaults would be formed in toughened glass. This seemed fundamental as they were external, very large in size (more that four metres long) and breakages were clearly

The rear elevation of the property prior to refurbishment.

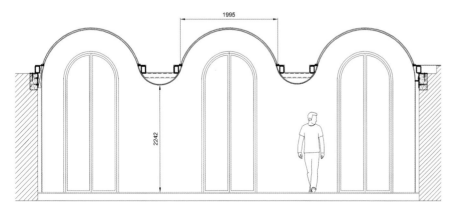

A basic section through the new rear extension, designed by Andy Martin Associates.

unacceptable. Apart from coping with the minor knocks and bumps of everyday life, the units were positioned such that one end could be in shade while the other was exposed to direct sunlight, therefore the possibility of thermal shock also had to be considered.

So we were very surprised when we were told that the glass contractor proposed to install double-glazed units manufactured using annealed glass. We were told that this was because large units with tight radiuses could be obtained more readily, and a very good manufacturer in Italy was willing to take on the work. It's true that the Italians are very good at manufacturing glass with single or double curves – you can see them in the windows of yachts, racing cars and so on – but we were very unhappy at the idea that the glass would not

The double-glazed vaults provide a unique roof covering to the internal space.

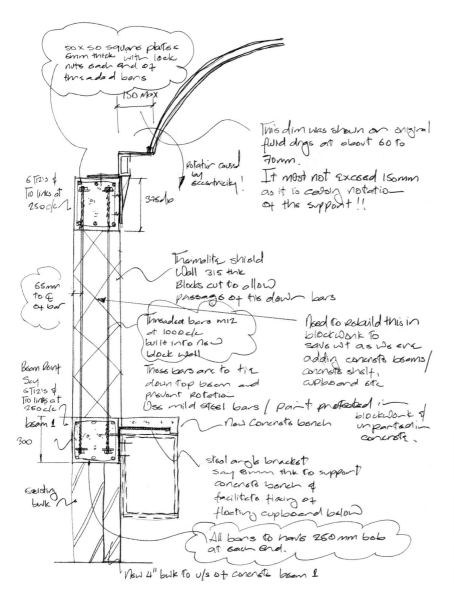

50 x 50 square plates 6mm thick with lock nuts each end of threaded bars

150 Max

Rotation caused by eccentricity!

This dim was shown on original fluid drgs at about 60 to 70mm.
It must not exceed 150mm as it is causing rotation of the support!!

6 T12's & T10 links at 250c/c

375dp

65mm to ₵ of bar

Thermalite shield Wall 315 thk Blocks cut to allow passage of this down bars

Threaded bars M12 at 1000c/c built into new block wall

These bars are to tie down top beam and prevent Rotation
Use mild steel bars / paint protected in blockwork & unprotected in concrete.

Need to rebuild this in blockwork to save wt as we are adding concrete beams / concrete shelf, cupboard etc

Beam Point Say 6 T12's & T10 links at 250c/c

beam 1

300

New Concrete bench

Existing bwk

steel angle bracket say 8mm thk to support concrete bench & facilitate fixing of floating cupboard below

All bars to have 250mm bob at each end.

New 4" bwk to u/s of concrete beam 1

A sketch of the tricky boundary condition, where the roof load, the horizontal thrust of the vaults and the concrete benches all have to be supported.

David Crookes with the project architect, Daniel Alvares, on the left and the contractor, Rupinder S. Lall, on the right.

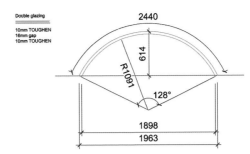

Double glazing

10mm TOUGHEN
16mm gap
10mm TOUGHEN

2440

614

R1091

128°

1898

1963

A section through the double-glazed unit by Cricursa, showing the shallower geometry they preferred.

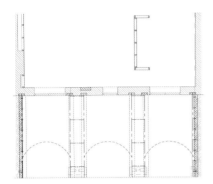

A plan view of the roof showing the position of the steel gutter beams that support the double-glazed vaults.

Images of the double-glazed, but not toughened, vaults made in Italy. Most of them failed!

be toughened. The contractor assured us that they had checked the units against thermal shock failure and that this would not be an issue.

Perhaps unsurprisingly, when problems did arise, the contractor quickly changed their tune, stating that the specification of the units was not their concern as their terms and conditions absolved them of any design responsibility. We found out later that the Italians had made five units for a very good price, but that three of them had failed before they left the factory. We can only surmise that they were so fragile that they were broken while being loaded onto the lorry. Thank God they did, as they would almost certainly have broken when they arrived on site. After this disaster it became clear that the only option was to return to our original specification. Cricursa in Spain are world renowned for their ability to manufacture curved, double-glazed units and this is where they were finally sourced. Acting on their advice, the units were not to as tight a radius as originally planned but, more importantly, they would be in toughened glass.

With the decision made to install these new units, the office relaxed a little as we felt that, at last, there was a very good chance of success. However, late in the day, the architects asked if the tie bar which restrained the glass arches against spreading could be omitted. The vaults are held in place at one end by the masonry wall of the existing house but, with no guaranteed lateral support at the garden end, we felt a tie bar here was essential. Removing this increased the risk of differential spread, which would result in very significant stresses and, most likely, failure unless the movement could be minimised.

In the original design, the tie bar had been concealed within the horizontal transoms at the top of the door frames, but the architects felt (rightly) that the design would be more elegant if the doors could follow the curve of the glass vaults. After much frustration and a good deal of lateral thinking, a scheme was developed where the whole door frame would act

The units were secured in steel cradles and craned into place over the main roof of the house.

as the necessary tie mechanism. Potential lateral movement due to the thrust exerted by the arches, particularly during the installation sequencing, was computer modelled with great care and diligence, which determined that the frames would be strong enough if fabricated from square, 70 x 70mm hollow section steel tubes. The architects were delighted with the solution and the project was quickly back on track.

Another complication was that the glass arches needed to be installed before the door frames were erected, which meant providing a temporary tie that could be cut out after the frames had been fitted. In order to ensure that the load was transferred to the frames as quickly as possible, it was decided to connect them to the vault support beams via a steel plate welded to the beams and drilled and tapped to the frame on site.

The units arrived safely and were lifted across the roof by crane before being manipulated, very carefully, into place. Each unit weighed in excess of 600 kilograms and required a lot of love and care while being manhandled into place, but all turned out well. The

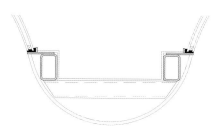

The support detail of the vaults was critical and needed to be uniform while allowing for the tight geometry.

With each unit weighing more than 600kg, installation was a very tricky process requiring delicate handling.

vaults were installed correctly, the temporary tie beams were removed without consequence, and we all went home happy with a large sigh of relief.

This was a difficult project and only those fully immersed in it will understand all the complications. The project architect, Daniel Alvares, a dedicated and thoughtful Chilean, was the key to its success. His particular educational background allowed him to appreciate the technical challenges that were evolving, while struggling to deliver the aesthetic vision of his boss and, hopefully, client. Sometimes, it takes a lot of engineering effort to achieve something that seems simple, quiet and serene.

The units in their protective steel cradles which were removed after they had been successfully located.

Finite element analysis of the vaults was carried out twice, first with a tie rod to limit horizontal spread (1) and then using only strengthened door-frames (2).

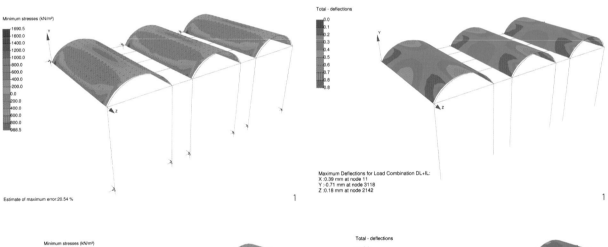

Minimum stresses (kN/m²)
1690.5
1600.0
1400.0
1200.0
1000.0
800.0
600.0
400.0
200.0
0.0
200.0
400.0
600.0
800.0
988.5

Estimate of maximum error:20.54 %

1

Total - deflections
0.0
0.1
0.2
0.3
0.4
0.5
0.6
0.7
0.8

Maximum Deflections for Load Combination DL+IL:
X :0.39 mm at node 11
Y :-0.71 mm at node 3118
Z :0.18 mm at node 2142

1

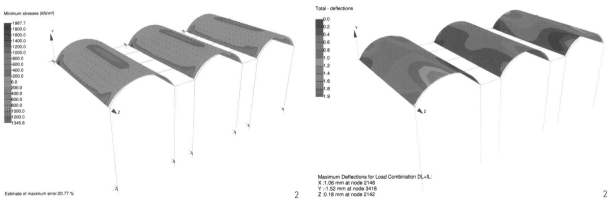

Minimum stresses (kN/m²)
1987.7
1800.0
1600.0
1400.0
1200.0
1000.0
800.0
600.0
400.0
200.0
0.0
200.0
400.0
600.0
800.0
1000.0
1200.0
1345.8

Estimate of maximum error:20.77 %

2

Total - deflections
0.0
0.2
0.4
0.6
0.8
1.0
1.2
1.4
1.6
1.8
1.9

Maximum Deflections for Load Combination DL+IL:
X :1.06 mm at node 2146
Y :-1.52 mm at node 3418
Z :0.18 mm at node 2142

2

View of the completed units as seen from the first floor.

Omitting the tie bars allowed the doors to be full height, which provided a more elegant architectural solution.

The double-glazed glass vaults create a memorable space that belies the complexity of the engineering that was required.

King Henry's Road Conservatory

The project at King Henry's Road was a glass extension at the rear of a large Victorian terrace house in north London. Unusually, the client, Paul Middelmiss, approached us directly, as he had a background as a furniture designer and had prepared some sketches explaining his ideas for the extension.

When we met, I said that I thought that the project would benefit greatly from the input of an architect and I recommended Paul Archer. We had collaborated with Paul several times previously on residential scale work, I admired his work and his ability to turn the most modest project into something special. In addition, I knew that Building Regulations and the various heating and cooling strategies would need to be resolved, and that Paul would bring an aesthetic refinement by his involvement.

Over the course of the first few meetings it became apparent that the client really did want an all-glass extension, or as near as was possible. We proposed two solutions with the glass cladding supported either by small steel beams and columns or by glass beams and

Proposals for the conservatory's structure began with a small steel frame (1), then a glass beam with glass fins (2), before finally developing the loadbearing glass wall idea (3).

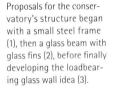
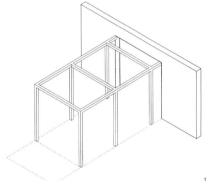
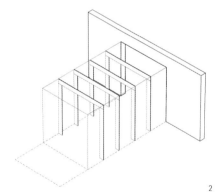
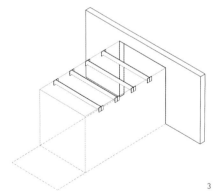

1

2

3

vertical fins. The latter was a technique that had been pioneered by Tim Macfarlane's office while working with the architect Rick Mather on a well-known house in Hampstead.

The concept for the extension was that it would, in effect, be a 'cardboard' box clipped onto the back of the house and separated from it by means of a pair of discreet sliding doors. This ability to separate the glass box meant that it could be categorised as a conservatory and not an extension, which allowed us to design the glass elements as laminated sheets rather than double-glazed units. This saved money, avoided the use of aluminium spacer bars (or their very expensive glass equivalent) and allowed the structure to be sealed with clear silicone rather than the black silicone normally associated with double-glazed units.

The finished glass conservatory with dining table and chairs set out for a lazy lunch. Note the door to the kitchen on the right.

The glass beams were carefully analysed to check the build up of stresses around the hole.

-10.8E6
-10.0E6
-9.00E6
-8.00E6
-7.00E6
-6.00E6
-5.00E6
-4.00E6
-3.00E6
-2.00E6
-1.00E6
0.00
1.00E6
1.11E6

In order for the box idea to work, the roof had to be installed as one laminated piece of glass that would act as a diaphragm. This would be laid to a minimum fall of about 0.5 degrees, while deflection due to self weight, snow and so on would be minimised by introducing glass beams at close centres to stiffen the roof. The client was enthusiastic about the scheme as a whole, but not the vertical fins (that would have been about 200mm deep on each side), which he felt 'cut' too far into the usable floor space. A decision was made to try to omit them and find an alternative way to support the beams directly off the glass walls.

Having considered the problem for a number of weeks, it was decided that bolting the beams might be an appropriate solution. A 'T' bracket was conceived, where the stem would slot into the triple-ply glass beams created by stopping the central glass elements short on each side. The table of the bracket would then be bolted to the glass walls, which consisted of two sheets of 12mm-thick toughened glass laminated together. The solution seemed practicable and appropriate for the scale of the project: the bracket would be easy to fabricate

A mock-up of a wall panel was constructed in F.A. Firman's workshop and tested, in set stages, to destruction.

in stainless steel and could be fitted with Sadev-type recessed bolts that can be bought on the open market.

Computer analysis of the proposed design indicated that the stresses would be acceptable in the area around the holes. However, a specific test of the fixing and associated glass support elements was called for as part of the tender documentation, which was won by F.A. Firman of Romford, one of the three or four leading specialist structural glass contractors in the country.

A trial part of the extension was erected in their factory and sand bags were slung from a glass beam to mimic snow loading at roof level. Once we were all satisfied that the bolt

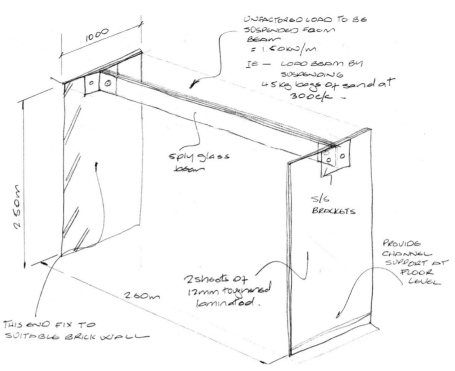

UNFACTORED LOAD TO BE
SUSPENDED FROM
BEAM
= 1.50KN/m

IE - LOAD BEAM BY
SUSPENDING
45Kg bags of sand at
300 c/c -

1000

2.50M

5ply glass
beam

S/S
BRACKETS

PROVIDE
CHANNEL
SUPPORT AT
FLOOR
LEVEL

2 sheets of
12mm toughened
laminated.

2.60m

THIS END FIX TO
SUITABLE BRICK WALL

A sketch of the partial mock-up that was specified in the tender, to test that the glass would perform as indicated by the calculations.

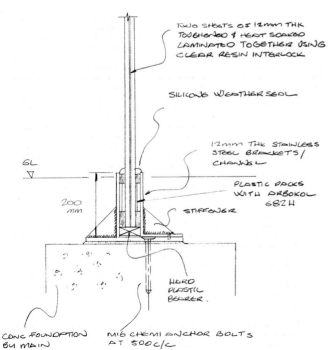

TWO SHEETS OF 12mm THK
TOUGHENED & HEAT SOAKED
LAMINATED TOGETHER USING
CLEAR RESIN INTERLOCK

SILICONE WEATHERSEAL

12mm THK STAINLESS
STEEL BRACKETS/
CHANNEL

GL

200
mm

PLASTIC PACKS
WITH ARBOKOL
682H

STIFFENER

HARD
PLASTIC
BEARER.

CONC FOUNDATION
BY MAIN
CONTRACTOR

M16 CHEMI ANCHOR BOLTS
AT 500 c/c

The glass walls were well anchored around the perimeter to ensure that they had good stiffness against lateral deflection.

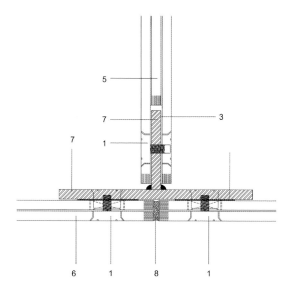

A plan *(left)* and side elevation *(far right)* of the metal bracket between the wall and glass beam, indicating:

1 12mm CSK fittings with (99.9%) pure aluminium liners
2 Roof in one section of glass made up with two layers of 8mm heat-soaked toughened glass laminated together
3 80mm diameter Klingrite disc to both sides
4 2mm rectangular black fibre gasket bonded to back of bracket, plus sandblasting to glass 3mm larger all round to conceal gasket from outside
5 Beams constructed with three layers of 10mm heat-soaked toughened glass laminated together with 2mm resin interlayer
6 Walls made up with two layers of 12mm heat-soaked toughened glass laminated together with 2mm resin interlayer
7 12mm thick purpose-made stainless steel bracket
8 Black structural glazing compound

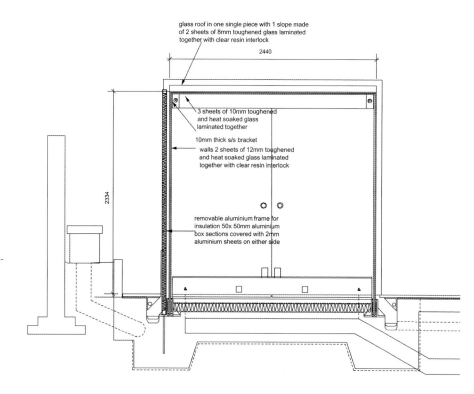

glass roof in one single piece with 1 slope made of 2 sheets of 8mm toughened glass laminated together with clear resin interlock

2440

3 sheets of 10mm toughened and heat soaked glass laminated together

10mm thick s/s bracket

walls 2 sheets of 12mm toughened and heat soaked glass laminated together with clear resin interlock

2334

removable aluminium frame for insulation 50x 50mm aluminium box sections covered with 2mm aluminium sheets on either side

Two sections through the conservatory showing the substructure venting ducts that blow either warm or cool air into the space depending on the time of year *(right)*, and the position of the glass beams and the make up of walls and roof *(far right)*.

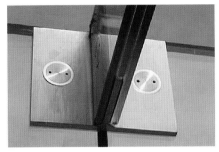

Two views of the stainless steel 'T' bracket that connects glass beam to glass wall.

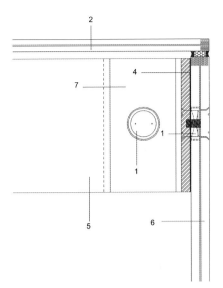

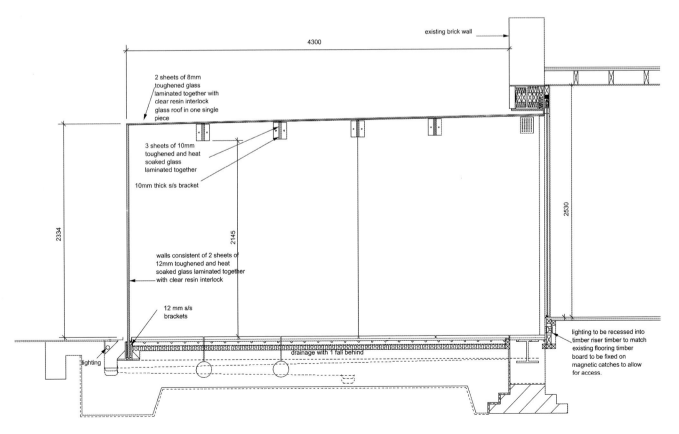

existing brick wall

4300

2 sheets of 8mm toughened glass laminated together with clear resin interlock glass roof in one single piece

3 sheets of 10mm toughened and heat soaked glass laminated together

10mm thick s/s bracket

walls consistent of 2 sheets of 12mm toughened and heat soaked glass laminated together with clear resin interlock

12 mm s/s brackets

2334

2145

2530

lighting

drainage with 1 fall behind

lighting to be recessed into timber riser timber to match existing flooring timber board to be fixed on magnetic catches to allow for access.

Inside the conservatory, with the view out to the garden unhindered by glass fins or mechanical fixings.

fixing was capable of safely transferring the shear loads, we went on to break one of the 12mm-thick sheets that made up the laminated glass wall. This was done with a centre-punch attached to the end of a long pole (and took several attempts before succeeding), but the system continued to function adequately, thereby validating the redundancy that is always essential when working with glass structures.

On site the project was broken up into two separate contracts, with the foundations and opening in the rear wall being completed by a local builder before F.A. Firman arrived to erect the glass structure. As part of this process, special mention had been made in the tender documentation to ensure the glass roof was fitted to very tight tolerances, as this was the only way that we could avoid the issue of water ponding on the roof, yet achieve the magical architectural requirement of what appeared to be a flat roof.

Fortunately, the glass industry has a history of working to tighter tolerances than those used when installing steel or concrete, and once we had calculated the deflection in the

Views of the conservatory under construction, including the extensive landscape work carried out in the garden.

A view from the end of the garden looking over the new pool.

roof due to snow loadings and the like, we knew exactly how much tolerance was left for the materials and the contractor's erection work. These were made explicit to the contractor who then made sure that his work met the necessary standards by continually checking his setting out and adjusting the roof glass levels throughout the construction. The roof was thus installed to everyone's satisfaction, after which the surface was treated with Ritec ClearShield to inhibit the build up of dirt.

In November 2004 this project won a 'Special' Institution of Structural Engineers Award for exceptional engineering, with the judges commenting that the project was, 'a wonderful response to a demanding brief [which] demonstrates that exceptional engineering is immune to scale'. We were all surprised and delighted, and to this day believe that it must be the smallest project ever to win such a prize.

The Spiral Stair

The spiral staircase came to us as a project thanks to the recommendation of John Evans, the owner of Ash Construction. John is a classic London builder always doing 20 things at a time. He can be a cheeky chappy, drives a white van, gets around a bit, but has a penchant for doing very fine contract work for London's up-and-coming architectural talent. The project involved the complete refurbishment of a town house near Hyde Park, which was to include a new mezzanine, designed as a library, that was accessed via a spiral staircase. The interior had a lot of dark stained timber and the interior designer had decided that the new staircase should act as a counterpoint to this by being constructed in glass, to give it a jewel-like quality.

When I met the client, he was a charming man and obviously very cultivated. We discussed the new stair and I pointed out that he could easily buy one from a reputable company, many of whom manufactured spiral staircases with glass treads. Alternatively, I suggested that he could engage us to design a bespoke staircase that would have the prerequisite glass treads, but also an all-glass central support column.

An early office-made model and a computer rendering of the proposed spiral staircase, prepared to help the client understand the concept.

The idea that a glass column could be made from assembling glass discs on a central rod had been around in engineering circles for several years. The theory was that when the rod was tightened up, the discs would be compressed and could act as a column. Glass is very good in compression and the vertical load being supported would be relatively minor. In order to explain the idea better I asked a very good glass contractor, Malcolm Armfield of Armfield Structural Glass, to make up a small assembly about 200mm high in polished low-iron glass so that I could show the client. I explained to him that, as far as we knew, the idea had never been built before and that if successful he would have something completely unique. The fall back position, if the technical challenges proved insurmountable, would be to use a polished

A view on the completed stairs showing the stacked glass discs and the evenly spaced stainless steel rings that support one end of the acrylic-backed clear glass treads.

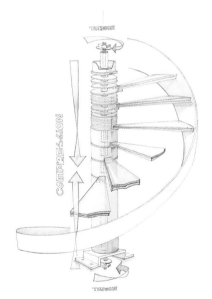

An early sketch showing the principle of using glass discs as a column to support the treads.

stainless-steel tube. In the end, the client agreed that we could undertake the design on the understanding that he would 'pay for a Jaguar but not a Maserati'. Not being au fait with car prices, I asked a work colleague what this meant and he said about £50,000.

We immediately set about testing the idea of building a column which would support the treads. The idea was to post-tension the assembly so that, even when a load on the treads induced moment into the column, the compression was such that tensile forces would never develop. The mathematics was simple enough and very quickly we had worked out what torque would be required in the central stainless-steel bar to keep the glass discs compressed. However, as is often the case, the maths or engineering analysis is only a part of the process

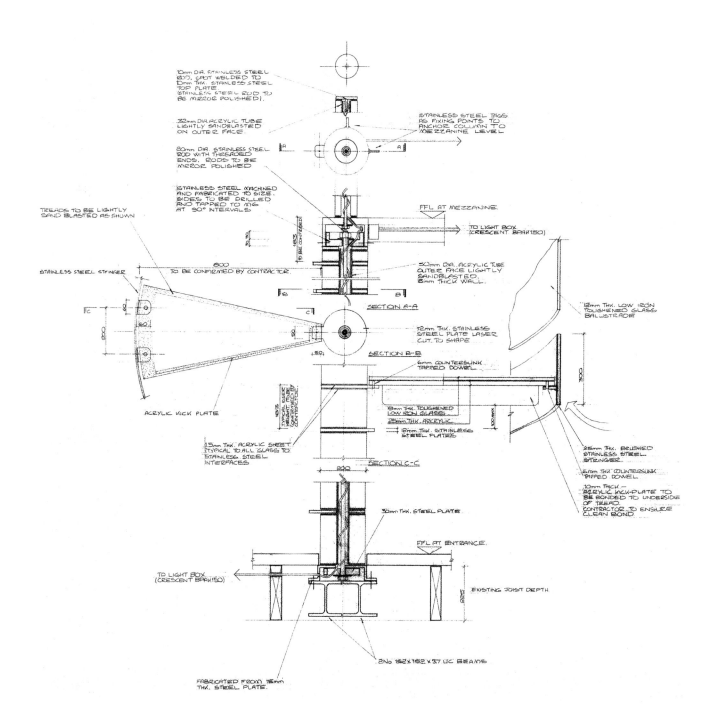

10mm DIA. STAINLESS STEEL
ROD, SPOT WELDED TO
10mm THK. STAINLESS STEEL
TOP PLATE
(STAINLESS STEEL ROD TO
BE MIRROR POLISHED).

32mm DIA. ACRYLIC TUBE
LIGHTLY SANDBLASTED
ON OUTER FACE.

20mm DIA. STAINLESS STEEL
ROD WITH THREADED
ENDS. RODS TO BE
MIRROR POLISHED

STAINLESS STEEL MACHINED
AND FABRICATED TO SIZE.
SIDES TO BE DRILLED
AND TAPPED TO M6
AT 90° INTERVALS

TREADS TO BE LIGHTLY
SAND BLASTED AS SHOWN

STAINLESS STEEL STRINGER

TO BE CONFIRMED BY CONTRACTOR

ACRYLIC KICK PLATE

15mm THK. ACRYLIC SHEET
(TYPICAL TO ALL GLASS TO
STAINLESS STEEL
INTERFACES

STAINLESS STEEL TAGS
AS FIXING POINTS TO
ANCHOR COLUMN TO
MEZZANINE LEVEL

FFL AT MEZZANINE.

TO LIGHT BOX
(CRESCENT BRAK150)

50mm DIA. ACRYLIC TUBE
OUTER FACE LIGHTLY
SANDBLASTED.
5mm THICK WALL.

SECTION A-A

12mm THK. STAINLESS
STEEL PLATE LASER
CUT TO SHAPE

SECTION B-B.

6mm COUNTERSUNK
TAPPED DOWEL

18mm THK. TOUGHENED
LOW IRON GLASS
25mm THK. ACRYLIC
12mm THK. STAINLESS
STEEL PLATES

SECTION C-C

30mm THK. STEEL PLATE

FFL AT ENTRANCE.

TO LIGHT BOX
(CRESCENT BRAK150)

EXISTING JOIST DEPTH

2No 152 x 152 x 37 UC BEAMS

FABRICATED FROM 15mm
THK. STEEL PLATE.

18mm THK. LOW IRON
TOUGHENED GLASS
BALUSTRADE

25mm THK. BRUSHED
STAINLESS STEEL
STRINGER.

6mm THK. COUNTERSUNK
TAPPED DOWEL

10mm THICK
ACRYLIC KICK-PLATE TO
BE BONDED TO UNDERSIDE
OF TREAD.
CONTRACTOR TO ENSURE
CLEAN BOND.

The finished assembly ready for testing.

A drawing by Armfield Structural Glass showing the assembly required to test the strength of the central glass column.

Assembly of the test-rig with its octagonal glass 'discs' located over the central bar. Apart from their shape, the discs matched the proposed specification for the glass exactly.

when innovative solutions are being pursued. It was clear that a trial assembly was required to explore the proposals more fully.

One of the leading questions was whether the glass discs should be made of annealed or toughened glass. Toughened was our instinctive choice, as each disc has a hole in it which can cause dangerous stresses in the surrounding glass. However, we also realised that if the glass was toughened and a failure did occur, then the disc would dice up and the whole assembly would need to be taken apart to replace it. Annealed glass might crack, but otherwise maintain its structural integrity. Another issue was how to treat the interface between the glass discs so that they could be safely clamped together. We were worried that grit might get between the discs and causing them to break when the tensioning bar was tightened up.

In the end a trial rig was assembled using a half-height column made from octagonal pieces of 12mm and 15mm thick glass. The glass was not toughened and the holes were CNC cut and polished. A very thin interface plastic material was cut out and placed between each

disc to isolate them from each other. The column was compressed and then tested using kentledge loaded on to a projecting steel beam to represent the load transferred from a tread. The testing proved successful and the project proceeded to manufacture and installation. The treads were fabricated using 19mm toughened low-iron glass 'taped' onto a 20mm thick acrylic sheet, which provided the necessary fail-safe mechanism. The acrylic was then supported at three points, two on the stainless-steel string and one on the column via a stainless-steel ring inserted into the column which incorporates a protruding 'finger' plate.

Additionally, a gimbal was manufactured which, in effect, acts as an adjustable three-legged stool located at the base of the column, which could be adjusted to ensure that the tensioning bar and glass column assembly would always remain plumb and true. This was an important consideration because a bar that was not exactly vertical was likely to induce

A key drawing: a hand-drawn sketch describing all the component parts of the staircase and its support structure.

uneven loads into the column. Incidentally, the use of low-iron glass for the column, treads and downstanding balustrade was not a structural decision, but one based on the clarity of this type of glass, thereby maximising its ethereal nature in the context of the dark, wood-lined interior.

Often, when I have spoken about the stair, architect friends have asked why the glass treads were not built into the glass column, so that the steel rings and finger plates could have been omitted. The engineering reasoning is simple in that rings (located at approximately 200mm centres vertically) make it far easier to replace damaged treads. If the treads had been built into the column, the whole staircase would have to be taken apart every time a scratched or damaged tread needed replacing. Would it have been worth it?

I don't know, as I was too busy worrying about the technical challenges. There are not many people who have a deep command of engineering issues, yet can look at a space or an object in a wholly poetic way, and I think this project goes to show that good design really does emerge from a harmonious dialogue between an architect and an engineer.

The trial glass column under test conditions: the discs were first compressed, then available material was added to replicate the final load transfer from a tread.

The actual glass column being trial assembled in the workshop. Note that the glass is now low iron type and that the octagonal discs have been replaced with polished circular ones.

The glass column temporarily supported on a levelling plate prior to manufacture of the final gimbal.

Assembly of the stainless steel levelling gimbal, which was essential to ensure the stair column was exactly vertical.

Trial tread support plates being considered for size and shape prior to their final design.

A close-up of the stair column during installation, showing the low iron glass discs, stainless steel tread support rings, and the acrylic fail-safe layer to the underside of the glass treads.

The glass column being assembled on the support gimbal, which will be concealed below the finished floor level.

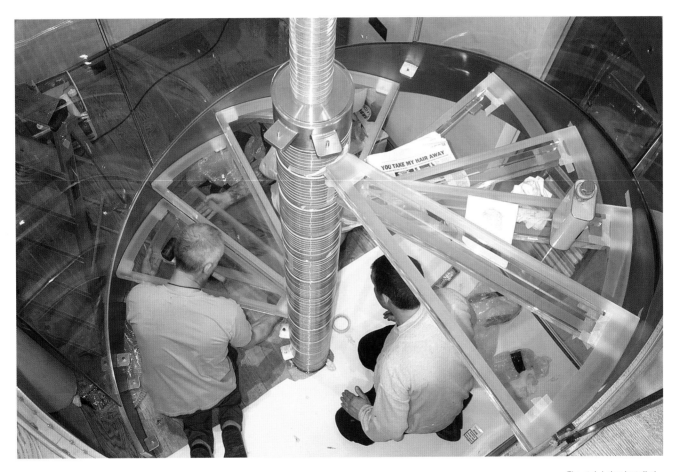

The stair being installed on site. Note the sand-blasted strips to the edge of the treads to reduce the risk of slipping and to mask the support plates.

The pool and its glass wall being tested by one of the design team prior to completion of the internal decoration.

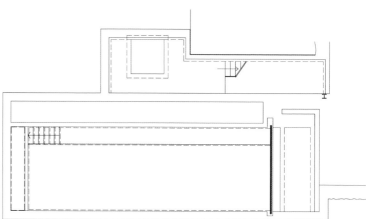

An early plan of the pool showing its basic dimensions of around 12 x 4 metres with a maximum depth of 1.2 metres.

Castelnau Swimming Pool

As a practice we have been involved in hundreds of house refurbishments in London. Many of these have involved the restoration or modernisation of Georgian or Victorian period properties. In some cases all we have to do is to create openings, to try to 'decompartmentalise' the historic spatial plans, while in others the work is much more widespread with barely the front facade being retained. For this project at Castelnau in west London, the work included widespread structural alterations, including a new basement area and a large rear extension. More importantly in this context, it also included a new swimming pool. This consisted of a waterproof concrete box which doubled up as part of the foundations for the new extension.

Late on in the project, the architect began to explore the idea of creating a glass retaining wall at one end of the pool to create a strong visual effect within the space. Glass walls in swimming pools are nothing new and in my memory I could remember that the architects Denton Corker Marshall had done one that cantilevered off the side of the roof of a hotel in Australia. I also had a faint recollection of one in New York, and of course we were very much aware of all the see-through walls that had been installed in the Rainforest Cafés and various waterworlds and aquariums.

Most textbooks advise that when glass is used to retain water, it should be annealed and laminated. This seems entirely reasonable as, should the glass be damaged or crack, it still has the ability to span between supports and offer good resistance to the water pressure. An alternative to using laminated annealed glass is to use acrylic, a robust material that has been used successfully in many instances including the London Aquarium. It can be cast in thicknesses up to 100mm and can be jointed almost seamlessly. It can also be installed with a concave profile, from which it draws extra strength.

An early concept sketch for the pool by Graham Massey of the scheme's architects, Creativemass.

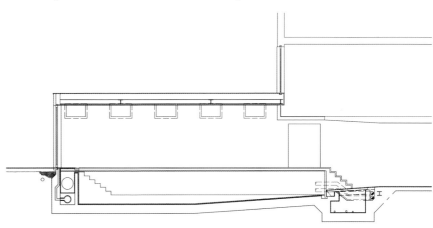

Section through the pool showing the variation in depth and the concealed troughs for overflowing water at either end.

In the case at Castelnau, however, the glass would be flat, with the added complication that it would not be supported along its top edge, as the pool was an infinity type. Pretty quickly, we established that we would need a large quantity of laminated float glass or a very costly and very thick acrylic wall. Neither was acceptable, so we decided instead to use laminates of toughened glass, working on the principle that one sheet would be designed to take the bending stresses induced by the head of the water, while the other acted as the required fail-safe. Toughened glass has an allowable bending stress of around $35N/m^2$ (unfactored), while annealed glass is generally designed for an allowable bending stress of no more than $7N/m^2$. By using toughened glass, therefore, we were going to be able to sustain a load five times greater for the same thickness, provided that deflection was not the governing criterion.

As is often the case with such projects, a problem arose in the office one weeknight just as everyone was planning to go home. John Graham, the project engineer, had been thinking about the water pressure on the wall and what other factors the glass should be

The glass wall weighed in excess of 500kg and had to be craned into place.

The glass wall being installed on site. Note the steel-lined 'pocket' in the reinforced-concrete side wall that has yet to be grouted up.

designed for. It occurred to him that a swimmer kicking against this end wall would cause a serious temporary load on the glass, and that this would certainly need to be accounted for. There are no British Standards for this – especially when the wall is in glass.

As an engineer you can feel pretty exposed when you have to decide what is a reasonable way to proceed. Obviously, the fundamental issue is that the wall must not fail. Not only would the whole basement be flooded and the swimmer knocked senseless, but there was also the threat that an irate client or developer would drag everyone off to court. With this in mind we began to imagine what possible scenarios would need to be addressed. What about the seven-foot-tall Olympic-standard Australian athlete in the pool? What about two of them racing each other? We worked into the night trying to determine what might be an acceptable criterion and how to turn that into a force we could calculate.

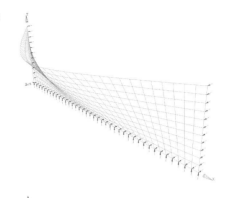

A computer model of the glass wall was built and tested for various load combinations to check the bending stresses and deflection.

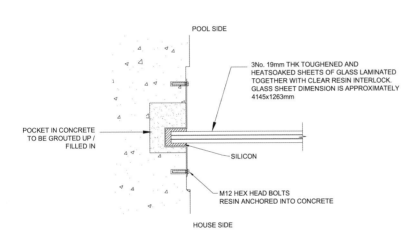

POOL SIDE

3No. 19mm THK TOUGHENED AND HEATSOAKED SHEETS OF GLASS LAMINATED TOGETHER WITH CLEAR RESIN INTERLOCK. GLASS SHEET DIMENSION IS APPROXIMATELY 4145x1263mm

POCKET IN CONCRETE TO BE GROUTED UP / FILLED IN

SILICON

M12 HEX HEAD BOLTS RESIN ANCHORED INTO CONCRETE

HOUSE SIDE

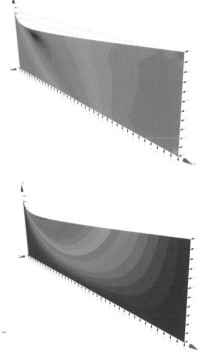

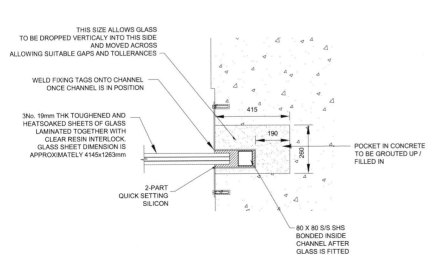

THIS SIZE ALLOWS GLASS TO BE DROPPED VERTICALY INTO THIS SIDE AND MOVED ACROSS ALLOWING SUITABLE GAPS AND TOLLERANCES

WELD FIXING TAGS ONTO CHANNEL ONCE CHANNEL IS IN POSITION

3No. 19mm THK TOUGHENED AND HEATSOAKED SHEETS OF GLASS LAMINATED TOGETHER WITH CLEAR RESIN INTERLOCK. GLASS SHEET DIMENSION IS APPROXIMATELY 4145x1263mm

415

190

260

POCKET IN CONCRETE TO BE GROUTED UP / FILLED IN

2-PART QUICK SETTING SILICON

80 X 80 S/S SHS BONDED INSIDE CHANNEL AFTER GLASS IS FITTED

Detail drawings of the edge supports at either end of the glass wall. Their exact location was critical and had to account for variations in the cast concrete.

The pool forms the centre-piece of the refurbishment of this Victorian basement and has transformed the nature of the space.

A section through the wall showing the support channel in the floor and the stainless-steel cap that protects the laminate interlayer material.

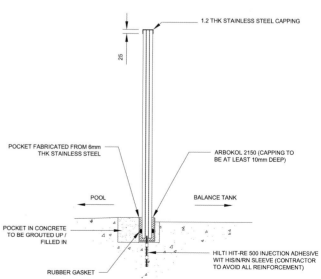

1.2 THK STAINLESS STEEL CAPPING

25

POCKET FABRICATED FROM 6mm THK STAINLESS STEEL

ARBOKOL 2150 (CAPPING TO BE AT LEAST 10mm DEEP)

POOL

BALANCE TANK

POCKET IN CONCRETE TO BE GROUTED UP / FILLED IN

HILTI HIT-RE 500 INJECTION ADHESIVE WIT HIS/N/RN SLEEVE (CONTRACTOR TO AVOID ALL REINFORCEMENT)

RUBBER GASKET

The water itself was not a problem, as it was only 1200mm deep and the design for the hydrostatic head was a relatively straightforward calculation. What we required was a way of determining the extra kinetic energy of a man kicking the wall as a force equivalent. Our solution was to design for the water pressure plus the equivalent force of one 100kg man jumping 600mm off the ground. Perhaps this is too onerous or perhaps it does not cover every scenario. It was a difficult call, particularly as no one would thank us for being overtly conservative and killing the project financially. The design was completed using the 100kg man, leading to a final glass specification requiring a laminate of three sheets of glass, each 19mm thick.

Very late in the day, an issue arose about the protection of the laminate material (a poured interlock, Uvicol or similar) against the water in the pool. The contractor, Tony Culmer of Culmax, feared quite reasonably that the chemicals and chlorine in the water might cause the interlayer to decay or possibly debond. As a cautionary measure, a stainless-steel channel was therefore bonded to the top of the glass wall to offer protection. I always thought that this was a harsh move, as it seemed to dilute the visual elegance of the glass wall at the point where the water laps over to be collected in a floor drain. It introduced a break where before there had been a seamless transition. We are not chemists, but with more time and commitment perhaps this issue could have been overcome.

The pool is visible through a glass floor at ground level – also engineered by Fluid Structures – so that children can be supervised at all times.

At night, lighting within the pool walls makes the whole pool glow.

The pool occupies a space at the rear of the house at the semi-basement level with access at the far end out to the rear garden.

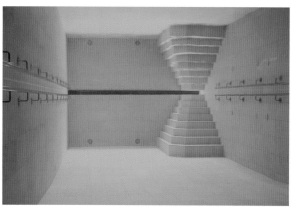

View of the pool beneath the waterline, showing the access steps at one end and the side rails.

View over the pool into the existing basement area, with the ground-floor living room visible through the glass floor and narrow clerestorey window above.

The rear of the house
with the glass doors from
the swimming pool area
in the foreground.

View of the glass canopy
on the west side of the
terrace, looking towards
Westminster.

The BAT Canopies

The design of the new canopies for British American Tobacco came to us from the architectural practice Researchitects, who had almost reached the end of their tether trying to win planning permission from the local authority. The fundamental stumbling block was that the canopies were to be a new addition on the seventh-floor terrace of the British American Tobacco's headquarters building. Located on the north side of the Thames, the terrace looks straight out onto the river, so the new canopies were going to be highly visible.

The client had previously provided shelters at lower levels where staff could take a break and have a cigarette, but those had been steel and glass affairs and the planning authority would not tolerate this approach at a more prominent and exposed location. We were asked, therefore, if we thought it might be possible to build new all-glass canopies, which would provide the shelter required yet meet the planners' strict visibility requirements. The design was simple enough, involving clear glass sheets supported on straightforward glass beams. These in turn were supported at the rear of the canopy on another glass beam supported off the existing structure, and at the front on glass columns located at approximately 1.5-metre centres.

The key detail in the design occurs where the glass beams are supported on the glass columns in a traditional mortice and tenon-type joint. Our initial wind assessment showed that

A design section through the canopy as drawn by Researchitects, showing the hidden gutter and the overhead heaters.

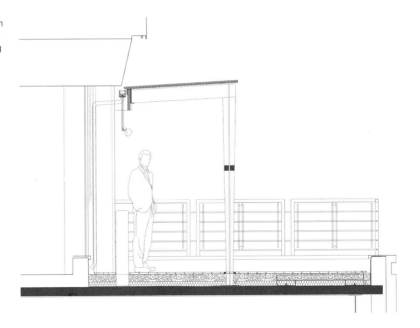

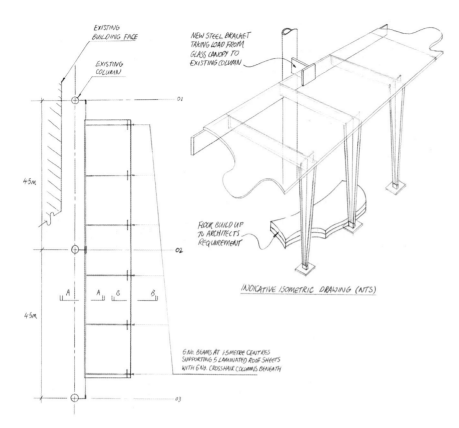

EXISTING BUILDING FACE

EXISTING COLUMN

NEW STEEL BRACKET TAKING LOAD FROM GLASS CANOPY TO EXISTING COLUMN

4·5m

4·5m

A   A   B   B

FLOOR BUILD UP TO ARCHITECTS REQUIREMENT

INDICATIVE ISOMETRIC DRAWING (NTS)

6 No. BEAMS AT 1·5METRE CENTRES SUPPORTING 5 LAMINATED ROOF SHEETS WITH 6 No. CROSSHAIR COLUMNS BENEATH

The original concept sketches prepared by Fluid Structures in response to brief by Researchitects.

A trial assembly of the beam and column was carried out in the work-shop to test the required tolerances.

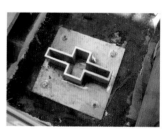

The metal base plate that holds the bottom of the cruciform glass columns in place.

the terrace was very exposed, where localised wind effects were likely to be amplified around the canopies. Under certain conditions the resulting uplift on the roof would expose the joints to very high forces. We decided early on that the structural silicone would not be sufficient and that a mechanical joint was definitely required. This needed to be simple and aesthetically acceptable, yet capable of dealing with the tolerance issues of the assembly.

In principle, the idea was that aluminium discs would be manufactured with a 2mm-thick, hard nylon sleeve fitted around their circumference. One of these would be inserted into a predrilled hole in the extended central sheet of the glass fin column, followed by one each in the two outside sheets of the glass beam. Once the cloumn and beam had been slotted together, a stainless-steel bolt would then be inserted in a hole passing through all three discs. Any mis-alignment between the three holes would be dealt with by drilling the discs after a trial assembly.

Thus, the process would be:

1) predrill a 12mm diameter hole in the centre of the first disc and insert in the column
2) erect beam and column as a mortice and tenon joint assembly
3) insert second disc in one of the outer sheets of the glass beam and mark the position of its 12mm hole through the hole in the column disc
4) remove disc and drill hole
5) repeat process for the third disc in the sheet on the other side of the glass beam
6) insert stainless-steel bolt into assembly through aligned holes in all three discs.

Following this procedure, each disc would be a tight fit in each glass hole and this would prevent the transfer of any wind uplift forces in a dynamic or jarring fashion.

Initially, the project went well and the glass contractor made good progress in erecting the glass beams, columns and sheets that form the canopy. However, on inspection, it was found that a number of the discs were loose in the holes. Indeed, some could be removed by hand and gaps of up to 2mm were measured on site.

The contractor huffed and puffed and said it was too difficult to achieve the tight fit specified; what had seemed straightforward in the workshop was proving very difficult on site. Whatever the reason, this was not going to be acceptable, but concerns were also being raised as to how to keep the project moving forward while this tolerance issue was resolved.

A series of construction details prepared by Matthew Turner of Fluid Structures showing the various glass junctions.

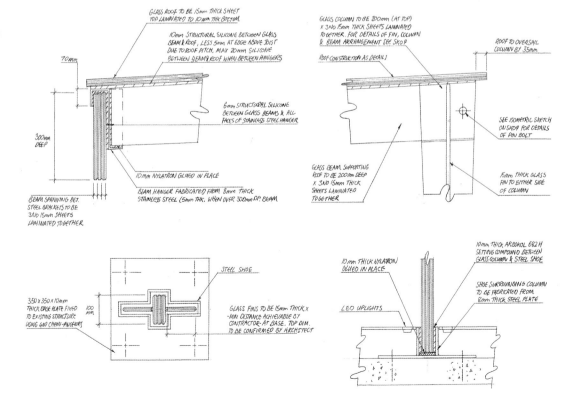

The east terrace canopy during construction.

Consideration was therefore given to the use of injectable resins to fill the gap, but some glues were too viscous and some too thin, while others were not compatible with the nylon or risked discoloration.

In the end, we stuck to the original specification and insisted that the contractor had to achieve a tight fit. As a consequence, he was required to re-measure all the holes on site with a digital micrometer, after which new discs were made on a lathe and fitted with new nylon rings manufactured by Elder Engineering Ltd to a tolerance of ±0.02mm. It turned out that the cost of making the nylon rings to such a high tolerance was relatively inexpensive and they could be supplied promptly, allowing the project to proceed satisfactorily to completion.

In hindsight, it is apparent that sometimes words are inadequate to describe what you are trying to achieve, and that a shared understanding can only be achieved by discussing the project as early as possible with everyone involved – including manufacturers and contractors. In future, I think we would also ask for full working mock-ups of the most important details prior to starting on site.

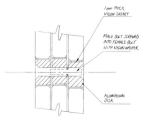

SECTION THROUGH BEAM & COLUMN

PIN BOLT ELEVATION

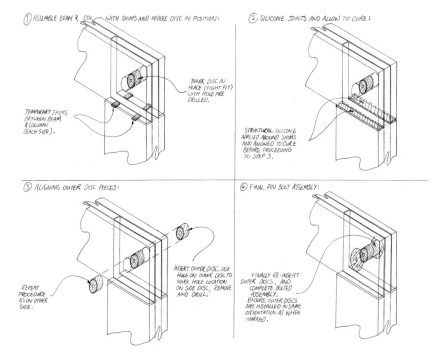

① ASSEMBLE BEAM & COL. WITH SHIMS AND MIDDLE DISC IN POSITION:

INNER DISC IN PLACE (TIGHT FIT) WITH HOLE PRE DRILLED.

TEMPORARY SHIMS BETWEEN BEAM & COLUMN (EACH SIDE).

② SILICONE JOINTS AND ALLOW TO CURE:

STRUCTURAL SILICONE APPLIED AROUND SHIMS AND ALLOWED TO CURE BEFORE PROCEEDING TO STEP 3.

③ ALIGNING OUTER DISC PIECES:

REPEAT PROCEDURE AS ON OTHER SIDE.

INSERT OUTER DISC, USE HOLE ON INNER DISC TO MARK HOLE LOCATION ON SIDE DISC, REMOVE AND DRILL.

④ FINAL PIN BOLT ASSEMBLY:

FINALLY RE-INSERT OUTER DISCS, AND COMPLETE BOLTED ASSEMBLY. ENSURE OUTER DISCS ARE INSTALLED IN SAME ORIENTATION AS WHEN MARKED.

Aluminium discs and a nylon '66' sleeve prior to drilling of the centre hole for the pin bolts.

A series of drawings prepared by Fluid Structures explaining the installation sequence for the discs and pin bolts.

GLASS

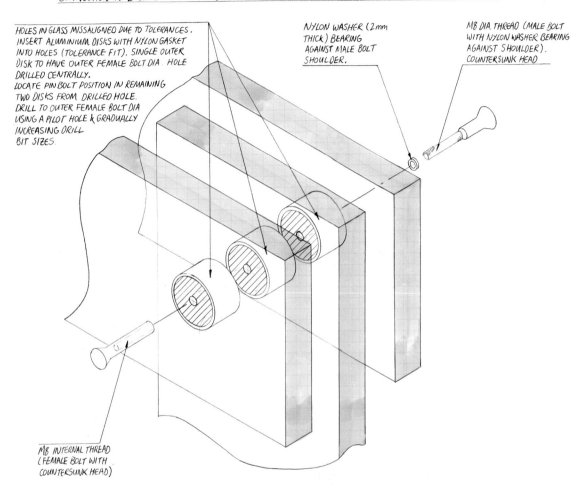

CONNECTION TO ENSURE EVEN DISTRIBUTION OF STRESSES AROUND HOLES WHEN FIXING PIN IS NON-CONCENTRIC

HOLES IN GLASS MISSALIGNED DUE TO TOLERANCES.
INSERT ALUMINIUM DISKS WITH NYLON GASKET
INTO HOLES (TOLERANCE FIT). SINGLE OUTER
DISK TO HAVE OUTER FEMALE BOLT DIA. HOLE
DRILLED CENTRALLY.
LOCATE PIN BOLT POSITION IN REMAINING
TWO DISKS FROM DRILLED HOLE.
DRILL TO OUTER FEMALE BOLT DIA
USING A PILOT HOLE & GRADUALLY
INCREASING DRILL
BIT SIZES.

NYLON WASHER (2mm
THICK) BEARING
AGAINST MALE BOLT
SHOULDER.

M8 DIA. THREAD (MALE BOLT
WITH NYLON WASHER BEARING
AGAINST SHOULDER).
COUNTERSUNK HEAD

M8 INTERNAL THREAD
(FEMALE BOLT WITH
COUNTERSUNK HEAD)

Detail view of the mortice
and tenon joint between
column and beam, detail-
ing the arrangement of
discs, washers and pin
bolt connections.

Detail views of the metal
shoe that supports the
end of the beam closest
to the building. The tube
below the shoe contains
a small external heater.

A detail view of the joint between a glass column and beam showing the pin and disc connection.

The cruciform columns and canopy roof almost disappear into the view.

A night view of the east terrace showing the LED lighting concealed in the recessed soffit of the glass beams and the uplighters to the columns.

Facade for Reiss

The Reiss headquarters building on Barrett Street came to us as a project in 2005. We had enjoyed a healthy working relationship with Reiss for some time, having worked with Dorrien Hopley of d_raw associates on a number of their stores throughout the UK. This had involved a good deal of normal structural work, but also glass stairs, chandeliers and bespoke pieces of furniture. When the headquarters building was mooted, he put us forward as engineers for the whole project, which was a big break for the practice.

The building had been the subject of a limited competition won by Michael Squire's practice, Squire and Partners, with a brief that called for a new-build, seven-storey building. The basement, ground and first floors would be given over to retail space, with offices above this and apartments on the top floors. The client was also very keen to develop a landmark building which would exemplify the brand and place Reiss at the forefront in the retail world.

We were duly engaged to provide the structural engineering input, which included the piled foundations, the new concrete superstructure, the lift shaft and so on. However, we

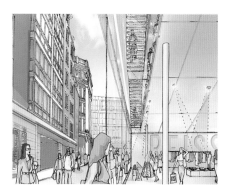 

Squire and Partners' competition images for the new Reiss headquarters on Barrett Street.

were also asked to act as facade engineers for the new Barrett Street elevation, which was fundamental to the scheme and clearly visible from the major shopping artery of Oxford Street. Initially, this was conceived as a more or less standard double-glazed facade, for which we considered a design based on planar fixings with a few variations to the established system. As a team, we investigated the use of colour films, dichromatic vinyls and so on, but none of these lent the facade the depth and variety that had been alluded to in the competition-winning illustrations.

Working with the M&E engineers, Hilson Moran, it became apparent that a double facade offered significant benefits to the performance' of the building, including noise abatement; a reduction in UV gain; the possibility of opening windows; extra cooling due to

The rain-screen facade at ground level, illuminated by concealed colour-changing LED lights.

FACADE FOR REISS

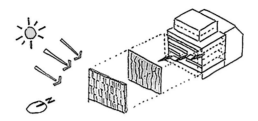

An early sketch by Squire and Partners showing their concept for the layered facade with its rain screen, double-glazed curtain wall and building structure.

the stacking effect within the void; and a lowering of energy costs. In the light of this, a new concept emerged where there would be an external rain screen separated from the double-glazed facade by a 600mm wide walkway. This would facilitate cleaning of the facade, while also acting as a device to aid the securement of the rain screen.

We started to look at constructing the rain screen with laminated glass or fused glass elements similar to those manufactured by Fusion Glass in Clapham, south London. The fused glass approach achieved the vertical stratification effect that was desired for the screen, but brought with it a number of problems – not least the inability to ensure a break-safe solution. If it was laminated to a toughened backing sheet, then we needed to be sure that the fused glass would also break safely on impact, which could not be guaranteed. Adding an additional front face of toughened glass was also considered, but this simply added more weight and, anyway, the laminating process between the fused and toughened glass was not proving straightforward. Even more frustrating was the fact that the fused glass did not really stand out enough and provide enough depth or articulation.

A photomontage of the new Reiss facade *(far left)* contrasted with views of Barrett Street as it was *(centre and left)*.

After several months of consideration, the facade was still not resolved and time was becoming tight. Marcie Larizadeh from Squire and Partners had been instrumental in driving the facade and was equally frustrated at the team's inability to address the technical requirements while achieving something special. Squire and Partners had made a number of small, but elegant plastic models to study the facade, and in a design meeting Marcie picked one up, turned to us and asked, 'Why can't it be like this?' In that moment the answer became apparent: we would make the rain screens from acrylic. As a practice we had good experience of the material. We knew it could be cast, cut with a saw, polished and worked. We had used it innumerable times as the fail-safe material on the underside of glass floors and treads. We also knew that there were specific issues about its use regarding fire, UV degradation and thermal expansion.

Fluid Structures was responsible for all the engineering aspects of the project, including the building's seven-storey concrete frame.

An early section through the double skin facade explaining the principle of the ventilated cavity.

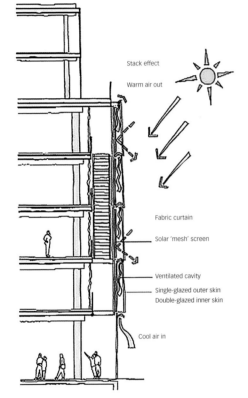

Stack effect

Warm air out

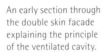

Fabric curtain

Solar 'mesh' screen

Ventilated cavity

Single-glazed outer skin
Double-glazed inner skin

Cool air in

Squire and Partners' drawing illustrating the benefits of the double-skin facade in terms of noise reduction and solar shading.

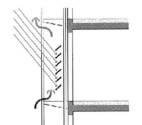

Double skin facade – interior glass remains cool

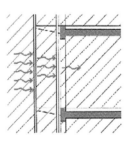

Improved thermal and acoustic performance

Screens high winds allowing controlled natural ventilation

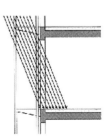

Increased natural light

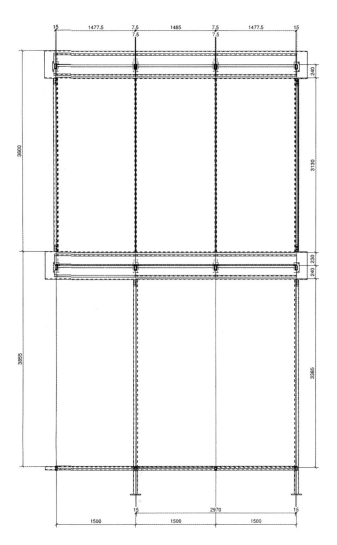

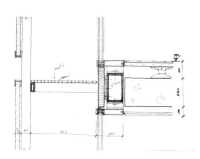

Right: Two sketches exploring how the acrylic skin might be restrained, while also taking account of its expansion.

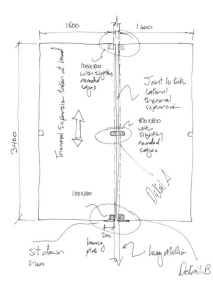

Part elevation of the new facade showing the key dimensions of the acrylic module.

The 50mm thick acrylic sheets can be routed, polished or sanded to create a wide range of visual effects and textures, from opaque to perfectly clear.

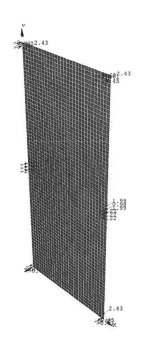

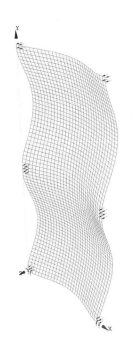

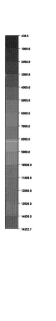

Computer models of the acrylic panels were prepared by Fluid Structures to explore the effectiveness of various support systems under different wind loadings.

A sample panel of acrylic prepared by Tuchschmid AG to show the possible range of finishes.

Sample panels were trial erected by Tuchschmid to examine the connections and further refine the methods of assembly.

Once we had decided, nothing could stop us. We visited a supplier and fabricator in the UK to discuss the sizes that could be obtained. We needed sheets at least 3.5 metres high, 1.5 metres wide and 50mm thick. The thickness was especially important as we intended to cut grooves into its outer face to achieve the vertical stratification that we had long been chasing. The material has come a long way since the 1970s – when it had established a poor reputation for discoloration and crazing – and the sheets we required were available. The UV issue could be resolved by mixing retardants into the batch, such that the material came with a 25-year guarantee against degradation. The fire issue proved to be less onerous, as the material was to be used outside the building line and could therefore be sprayed with another retardant.

The major issue was thermal movement, and this involved our office in a 'first principles' investigation into how best to secure the sheets to the building. Given that over a 60° Celsius temperature range the acrylic could expand over its length by up to 15mm, it was soon apparent that conventional bolting would not be an option. We decided, therefore, to support the acrylic sheets in loose-fitting stainless-steel shoes, which could be clipped back to the facade at the intermediate and upper levels. Hurried along by Marcie's enthusiasm, design drawings were prepared showing the acrylic rain screens supported, via the steel shoes, off mullions hung from the top of the building. Given the visual importance of these fixing details, we were encouraged to make them smaller, smaller, smaller, until all the parties were satisfied.

After the facade scheme had been developed, we worked with the architects to prepare the final specification so that the work could be tendered to specialist facade contractors. There are not many people with the detailed experience of acrylic we required, and we were worried that we wouldn't find anyone who would really engage with the project

Early sketches illustrating how a mechanical restraint might hold panels in place while allowing for thermal expansion.

Early computer renderings prepared by Squire and Partners to show the lighting effects they hoped to achieve.

The use of mock-ups is highly recommended, helping to clarify structural issues and assembly methods, and allowing architects to consider modifications to improve the aesthetics.

Test facade showing how LED lighting installed in channels at the bottom of each sheet would bathe the building in different colours.

The test rig proved invaluable in allowing the architect, engineer and manufacturer to identify the best solutions to a wide range of problems.

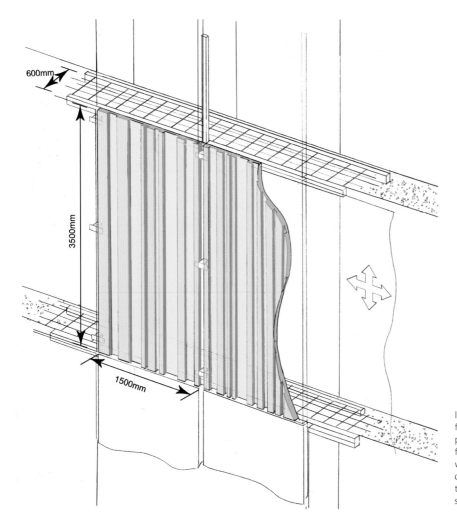

600mm

3500mm

1500mm

Isometric drawing of the facade, showing the support channels extending from the access walkways and the mechanical clips, three to each side, that hold the acrylic sheets in place.

and reach out to maximise the visual potential of the facade. But that was before we met Walter Luessi of Tuchschmid AG, a relatively small Swiss company that specialises in bespoke fabrication, one-offs and the kind of thing the bigger (and more boring) system companies try to avoid. Tuchschmid took the design and, with the architect's support, refined the concept.

They built mock-ups to examine the proposals, which allowed the system to be investigated visually. They also refined the clip system by cutting a full-height vertical recess into the edge of the 50mm-thick acrylic panels, so that a continuous, fully concealed rod restraint could be inserted. There is no doubt this process of making, testing and refining played an essential part in ensuring a satisfactory outcome for the facade. All the drawings and calculations in the world could not cover the ground or resolve the issues that the mock-ups allowed us to examine.

The Reiss facade is the largest acrylic facade in Europe and has attracted great critical acclaim since its installation, not least when the Reiss building was nominated for the World Architecture Awards in 2008.

The acrylic rain screen stops short of the main display windows and the entrance to the shop to allow customers a clear view of the merchandise on sale.

At night, the acrylic
facade gives the building
an ephemeral glow of
subtly shifting colours
that has created a new
landmark in the city.

The clean lines of the
facade continue inside
the shop.

FACADE FOR REISS

Masonry

Masonry

For a long time masonry did not really appeal to us as a practice. It seems a perfunctory material, found everywhere, part of the fabric of our lives but not sexy, not twenty-first century. It did not fit in with the idea of a modern society where buildings were led by technology and newer materials were waiting to be discovered. Slowly this changed and, as a practice, we became more receptive as our knowledge of the built environment grew. Three people have been a big influence on our thinking. The first was Bill Curtin, an insightful British engineer who pioneered the use of reinforced masonry in the UK between 1960 and 1980. He saw masonry as a low-cost material with good buildability and great potential in the postwar construction industry.

By reinforcing masonry he improved its bending resistance to wind loading and increased its capacity to carry vertical loads. This reinforcing work was not complicated and involved relatively low technological processes. His buildings often involved 'quetta' bond brickwork (13") with centrally placed reinforcing bars or, later, diaphragm walls with varying

The Pumping Station (far left) and The Judge Institute of Management Studies (left), two of John Outram's more distinctive brick projects.

Structural brickwork has a long and distinguished history, including their use in the railway viaducts of the Victorian era.

thicknesses depending on their height. I remember studying his projects for swimming pools, gymnasiums, schools and sports halls, and being impressed by the range of buildings his proposals addressed.

With brick diaphragm walls, the masonry forms the structure, the cladding and the lining. There are no steel columns to be hidden or fire protected, nor are there corrosion issues associated with components buried within other elements. More than that, I'm not sure that the power and beauty of his work ever really occurred to him. I know that we've been very influenced by his buildings and the Thaxted House project included in this book is a kind of homage to his greatness.

Another influence has been the British architect John Outram, whom I met several years ago. In a drunken debate with friends we had been discussing the great 'outsiders' of British architecture. Several were nominated and dissected, but John's name was always to

Bill Curtin's influential book on reinforced and prestressed masonry *(right)* includes descriptions of brick diaphragm walls that combine great vertical strength with good wind resistance *(below)*.

Design of **Reinforced and Prestressed Masonry**

W. G. CURTIN, G. SHAW and J. K. BECK

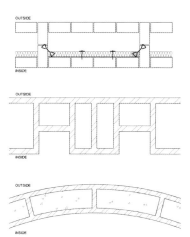

Bill Curtin's reinforced brickwork, often shaped into flowing forms, introduced a new sophistication into the use of structural brickwork.

the fore. He is clearly one of the most original architects of his generation, although he has not managed to build anywhere near as much as his peers. His two most famous buildings in the UK are probably the Pumping Station in London's Docklands and The Judge Institute of Management Studies at Cambridge University.

John is a polemicist and has strong, even mystical, views about materials and how they should both be expressed and used. He is a great champion of brickwork and how it embodies what he calls the 'humble spatial module'. He writes interestingly about the fact that bricks are made of clay and that their manufacture, the way they are fired, makes them 'feel' warm. This is in contrast to many modern materials such as plastic, rubber, foam and so on where the manufacturing processes are heavily industrialised and their distasteful odours betray their poor environmental credentials.

John's views have been condemned as outdated or extreme, but at least his position is clear: he sides with art, craft and workmanship. His is an architecture of ideas and themes, with a romantic vision and a belief in the designer's responsibility to uplift the human spirit. His work is not cool or clean and he never really embraced the 'aluminium pods and bubbles' of Modernism. Irrespective of where you stand and what you think of his work, his case for brickwork is astute and well reasoned. He sees each brick as a 'piece of cubic space that fits the human hand', in a way that allows it to be easily carried and deployed. These qualities, combined with its simple joint systems and an ability to be impervious to the elements, make a decent case for brick to be reconsidered as a sophisticated material with a far greater lifespan than most of its contemporary rivals.

Finally, I have to mention the Uruguayan Eladio Dieste, who practised as an engineer, architect and very much a hands-on builder in South America. Our office knew little of his work until recently, but a number of books have now been published which help to document his genius and illustrate how he redefined masonry construction and elevated it to a structural art form.

He set up in practice in 1955 (in Montevideo) at the age of 38 and his office became involved in a wide range of typical building projects, ranging from factories and shopping

Sun-dried clay bricks are still a major building material in many parts of the world.

centres to petrol stations and sports halls. He chose to avoid the reinforced-concrete constructions of many of his contemporaries in South America, but instead made use of locally manufactured clay bricks. As an engineer he tried to avoid what he called 'the tyranny of the plane', whereby all engineering solutions boil down to a hierarchy of simple components resolved in two dimensions, repeated to deal with the third. He preferred to develop three-dimensional structural forms which fully resolved the various loads he was dealing with.

Eladio Dieste championed a number of brick arch techniques to roof over buildings, the most innovative of which was the Gaussian vault. Using this system he created thin brick arch vaults with ceramic tiles in double curvature, to achieve spans in excess of 50 metres. He appreciated this ability to construct double curvature forms that age well and are lighter than concrete. He also realised that the use of continuous brickwork for curved elements in the vertical was a far more sensible and cost effective solution than concrete with its complicated formwork and impossible to hide construction joints.

He married brickwork's high compressive strength with catenary forms and developed simple, tensioned-steel reinforcement systems to ensure that the masonry always stayed in compression. I would strongly recommend that anyone interested in brick as an engineering material should investigate his Church of Christ the Worker, which was completed in 1960, and his later Church of San Juan de Ávila in Madrid. These buildings, designed without an

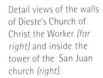

Detail views of the walls of Dieste's Church of Christ the Worker *(far right)* and inside the tower of the San Juan church *(right)*.

architect's contribution on limited budgets, encapsulate the strength of his ideas and are both structural tours de force and very well resolved pieces of architecture.

These are religious buildings built for local workers, using local materials, with a spirit that captures the new liturgical thinking that was developing in the Catholic church at that time. The fluidity of the curves and the naturalness of the construction puts to shame a host of more contemporary 'biomorphic' buildings that fail to read as well as these humble yet sophisticated low-cost buildings.

Thaxted Residence

David Birkbeck is a well-known journalist and director of Design for Homes. He is active in the world of housing and is a great champion of improving both the way we build and the environmental performance of our building stock. When he set about building his own home, he wanted to engage with new techniques to create a home that had minimal ongoing energy costs, setting a standard that would be an exemplar for contemporary living.

We came late to the project; in fact, I believe we were his second or third engineers – I'm not really sure which. However, I can say that I saw a previous scheme that was well worked up in structural steelwork, although pretty old fashioned in its approach. The concept for the house was to build an L-shaped spine wall that would act as a spatial separation device, ordering the plan and defining different living zones. The wall would also act as the building's service core, containing chimneys and 'ducts' for service runs, as well as providing a large volume of cooling brickwork whose thermal mass would help with the diurnal temperature variations.

A block from Hanson's Aversa range measuring 327mm long by 215 high by 90mm thick.

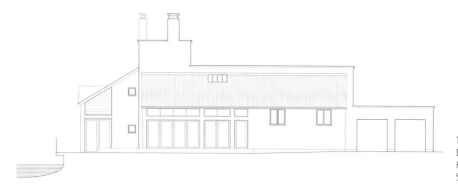

The bedroom wing of David Birkbeck's new house as designed by Snell David Architects.

When we met, the architectural scheme had been finalised but the engineering and the method of building was all up for grabs. After some careful consideration, it seemed to us that the house could be built in masonry and timber alone, completely free of steelwork. David also had the support of several of the country's leading contractors and building material suppliers which brought its own benefits, as they were all keen to introduce some of their latest technologies to the project. The foundations, for example, were designed and installed by Roger Bullivant's company, who proposed using a hybrid concrete and polystyrene ground-floor slab. The masonry was supplied by Hanson, while Finnforest provided the upper floors and roof, which were installed with significant amounts of insulation to achieve a very low U value.

The garden elevation of the completed house overlooks woodland and a local water course.

The side elevation of the house showing living accommodation sited on each side of the L-shaped spine wall.

The completed spine wall with the single-storey supporting shear walls under construction on either side.

From early on in the project, we realised that wind loading on the building would be the critical design criterion from a structural engineering perspective, and this would act on the spine wall. Although attractive as an architectural device, the spine wall — which stands more than eight metres high — was in structural engineering terms a towering spinnaker, ready to catch the wind and likely to be blown over during construction or when the first winter storm occurred. The wall was to be built using large white clay blocks measuring 327mm long by 215mm high by 90mm thick from Hanson's Aversa range but, although the wall was designed as a diaphragm some 660mm thick, it could not possibly resist the wind loads associated with a one in 50 year storm.

The new floors and roofs which spanned to the wall were in timber and, while economic in their means and cost, they did not provide nearly enough weight to keep the spine in

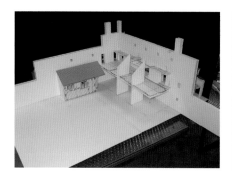
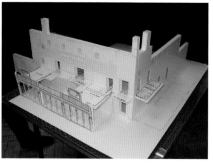
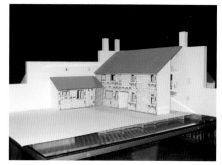

We made a cardboard model of the house to explore the stability of the spine wall in high winds.

compression. Thus, the fundamental issue was how to stabilise the house while staying true to the architectural concept. Compounding our concerns, it soon became apparent that the client was keen to vertically stack bond the blocks of the spine, rather than construct the masonry in a normal stretcher or Flemish bond. There was no alternative, therefore, but to recommend using a technique involving resin mortars. In this system, a pre-mixed resin-based mortar is delivered to site, where water is added to achieve a suitable workability. By using resin mortars, the masonry is better able to develop some degree of flexural tension and thereby better resist wind forces.

Paul Rogatzki (of Hanson Building Systems Research) was instrumental in helping us to develop the solution. His team had previously carried out research in the area and knew what increased flexural bending stresses could be achieved. Working from this higher figure of 1.35 N/mm^2 as opposed to a more conventional 0.7N/mm^2, we were able to prove that the proposed spine wall was thick enough to withstand the force of even the most onerous wind

A view of the spine wall under construction with one of the cross-walls visible in the foreground and concrete padstones in place to receive floor and roof joists.

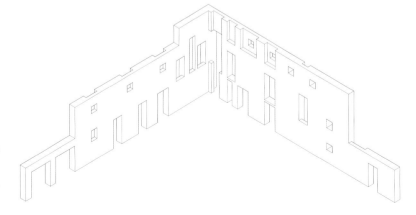

Isometric view of spine wall produced by Hanson showing openings and variations in thickness of the diaphragm.

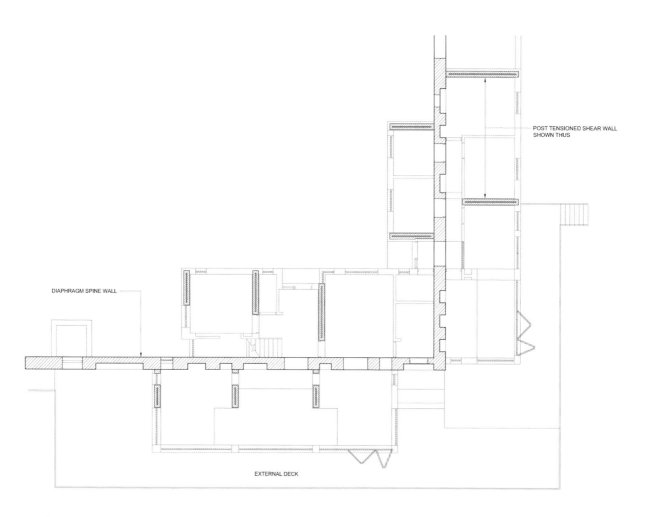

POST TENSIONED SHEAR WALL
SHOWN THUS

DIAPHRAGM SPINE WALL

EXTERNAL DECK

A plan view of the spine wall showing the orthogonal post-tensioned shear walls needed to resist wind loads.

Application of the resin mortar that binds the blockwork together. Note the use of bedding reinforcement to ensure a thin joint.

Two views of the structural timber floors and roof that form the main accommodation of the house on either side of the spine wall.

Sketch section by Fluid Structures explaining how the post-tensioned shear walls work.

Images of the diaphragm wall under construction, showing the recesses to accommodate storage zones and services.

A view of the house from the garden showing the spine wall and the external deck beside the water course – much loved by the client's children.

conditions. We were jubilant with the outcome of the calculations. It meant that the concept could be maintained and the blocks could, indeed, be stack bonded. Moreover, the thickness of the horizontal bed joints would necessarily be reduced to improve the adhesion between the blocks, thus increasing the unique visual nature of the spine.

The work on site progressed slowly, because the bricklayers were initially wary of the process. Problems were encountered with the viscosity of the mortar mix and, in the early stages, bed joint reinforcement was used as a temporary spacer between the blocks. To further reduce the wind induced moments in the spine wall, it was also decided to tie the wall at first floor level, via the timber floor diaphragm, to orthogonal blockwork walls that would act as shear walls. These were constructed in pairs of 100mm thick blocks with a 50mm gap between them. As the floors weighed so little, it was necessary to post-tension the shear walls at each end with stainless-steel tie bars, anchored in the foundations and passing through a concrete capping beam that straddled the two leafs of blockwork.

This process of post-tensioning masonry is used infrequently nowadays in the UK. It is, however, part of the lexicon of techniques that the engineer Bill Curtin had developed and refined in the 1970s and '80s, when his system of building masonry diaphragm walls with post-tensioning bars had allowed a whole range of municipal buildings, from swimming pools to fire stations, to be built without the use of steel frames. Thus, with its use of resin bonded diaphragm walling and post-tensioning, the Thaxted House represents a small homage by our office to Bill Curtin's work, which made it all the more rewarding when the project received the Brick Development Association's award for the Innovative Use of Brickwork in 2005.

Loop Architecture responded to the attributes of
prefabricated brick panels
by developing a scheme
based on stepped forms
and dramatic cantilevers.

Oldham Housing

Europan, Europan, Europan – why do we enter these competitons? I don't really know why ...

Shortly after the completion of the Thaxted House, I got together with three very talented young architects who were banding together to enter competitions. Alex Franklin, Phil Catcheside and James White worked for various practices and were making fledgling moves towards setting up together in practice – to be called Loop Architecture. What they needed was a competition win and a juicy commission to proceed with. Over the course of several evening meetings, we discussed a competition brief for a small area of social housing in Oldham. They brought their ideas about housing, urban planning, how we should live and the definition of a street, while I put forward ideas about how to build in a contemporary manner that would improve on traditional English methodologies. We wanted to build in brick and timber, but we wanted to re-explore the potential of the materials and draw on practices from Europe — particularly Holland.

I have to confess that my ideas had been very much influenced by a Dutch engineer, Harrie Vekemans, whom I had met during a trip to Antwerp while designing the Thaxted House.

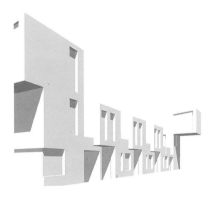

Exploratory massing drawings by Loop Architecture, emphasising the modular nature of the prefabricated masonry concept.

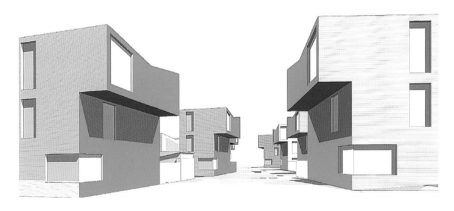

Harry knew that I was a hardworking engineer in the UK, but when I explained my marvellous tricks with resin and post-tensioning, he had laughed, explaining that in Holland they did this — and much more — every day. The truth was that he was right. As an engineer, he ran his own practice, Adviesbureau Vekemans, that specialised in masonry. He built multi-storey buildings in masonry; he post-tensioned brick marine walls; and he had even devised a system for erecting buildings using brickwork with no mortar bedding, known as 'Click Brick'. I was charmed more than offended, but did point out that while a lot of the work was extremely innovative by UK standards, some of the buildings looked, shall we say, rubbish. He wasn't easily offended and we became good friends.

A prefabricated masonry housing scheme in Holland during and after construction – images courtesy of Adviesbureau Vekemans.

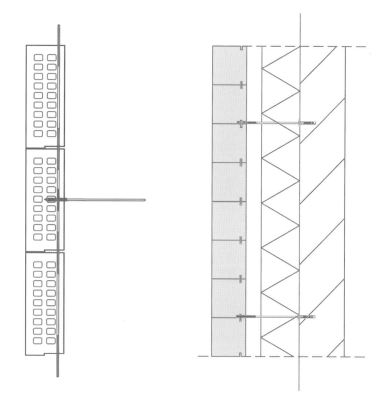

A plan view of the 'Click Brick' system showing how the outer skin of mortar-free brickwork is mechanically tied back to the inner structure.

A housing scheme in Holland that uses the 'Click Brick' system.

Sample panels of the 'Click Brick' system using bricks of different colours.

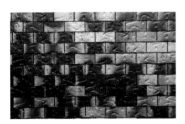

Detail views of the 'Click Brick' system showing the outer skin of mortar-free brickwork tied back to the inner structure, with or without cavity insulation.

It was in Holland, however, that I saw the real potential for glued masonry. Large panels were constructed in factories and glued together in almost the same way as precast concrete. These could readily incorporate window openings, they could cantilever significantly and could be lifted with relative ease due to the strength of the resin mortar and the quality of the prefabrication. Other panels came with insulation on the back, with pre-installed balconies, or with load-bearing inner walls. I was excited and saw the opportunity to incorporate these ideas into the competitions we were entering.

At Oldham, our structural ideas were very straightforward. We would prefabricate the external masonry panels and use them structurally to support the timber floors. In this way we could cantilever out where we wanted and bring a freedom to the floor plans not offered in

Loop Architecture's masterplan for the whole scheme, showing how the site was to be laid out in cranked rows with a hierarchy of family houses and adjoining mews.

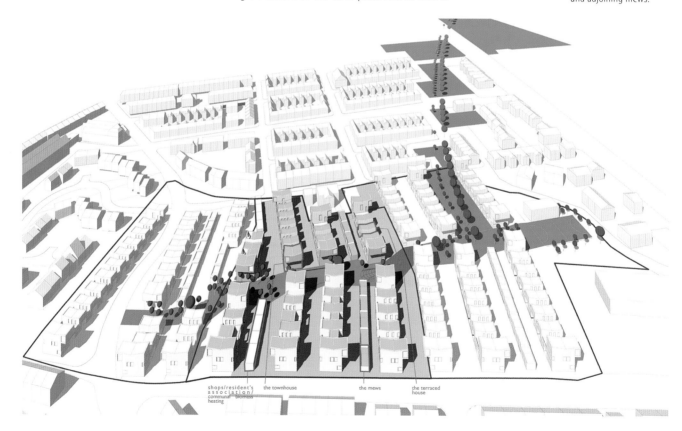

shops/resident's association/communal biomass heating   the townhouse   the mews   the terraced house

MASONRY

The scheme broken down into various house types that seek to optimise repetition and thus simplify prefabrication.

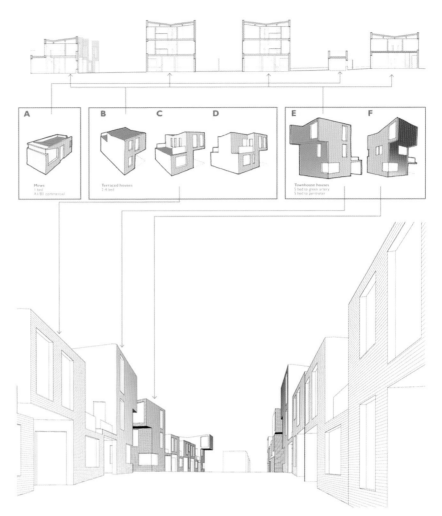

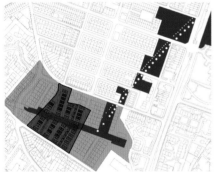

Plan of the scheme showing the proposal for a series of linked green spaces.

conventional masonry techniques. In addition, we would build the floors with pre-engineered timber joists (Steico, Masonite and so on), and where we wanted longer spans we would use Kerto high-strength engineered timber beams to avoid having to add steel beams or lintels.

This use of masonry in prefabricated panel form had a significant effect on the visual depiction of the scheme. I would not say that this was the only factor, as the scheme was well worked up with considerable attention to detail and architectural rigour, but the result was that the architects were able to submit a lovely set of drawings. The outcome was that we won and joined that victorious list of architects and engineers who have won a Europan competition in the UK, but have never managed to top out a winning scheme.

I often think about Harrie and his practice that specialises in brickwork. I don't think such a company could exist in the UK, where engineers are expected to be able to deal with at least four or five materials comfortably. To date, we have never had the chance to use 'Click Brick', and I don't think it has ever been used in the UK, but we'd love to give it a go.

A view of a typical street emphasising the scale of the development and the variation in house types.

Streets would have been bookended with three-storey townhouses to provide reference points in streetscape.

Children would have been able to play safely in the open and green spaces that permeate the scheme.

The Open and Shut House

We have worked with the architects Toh Shimazaki for several years and have watched their practice grow in concert with ours. They are a very interesting bunch led by Yuli Toh, a Malaysian woman, and Takero Shimazaki from Japan. Initially, their projects were small, but over the years they have grown in size. They bring a slightly different sensibility to their work compared with other British practices, putting forward ideas that certainly draw on their UK architectural education but are also rooted in a different culture. When the opportunity arose to work with them on a new 'weekend' house for a London family, we were very pleased to get the commission.

The OSH (Open and Shut) House is located in Surrey's green belt and was planned as a weekend retreat, where the clients could escape to with their children. It was important, therefore, that it could be easily closed up when they were not there. In many ways, the house is a take on the English Arts and Crafts tradition, yet updated and modernised for contemporary living. It also needed to be built simply and economically, and for that reason it was decided that the predominant structural materials should be brick and timber. When we sat down with

Study collage and models prepared by the architects Toh Shimazaki to explore how the house might fit into the site's topography.

the architects to explore the form, however, we were keen to establish a narrative that would tell the structural story of the house and why it was the way it was.

We explored lots of structural ideas during these early discussions. Conceptually, the house was straightforward enough, with load-bearing walls supporting the roof. In this way, the lateral wind forces on the main elevations would transfer up to the roof which, acting as a diaphragm, would transfer the forces onto the orthogonal gable walls, which would act as shear structures. In order to further stabilise the brick facades, we also considered steel framing, wind posts and so on, but nothing really appeared to 'belong' to the scheme or bring harmony to the elevations.

After several meetings we began to explore the 'zoning' of the masonry, defining the inner leaf, the cavity zone and the outer skin. We decided that we could strengthen the outer skin with masonry piers, and that those piers would have a simple hierarchy. Where the walls

The engineering narrative of the house is sensed in the 'muscularity' of the external brickwork and its prominent piers.

were tall, the piers would be bigger as they were resisting more wind force. Equally, where they were closely spaced, they could reduce in size. Using this simple strategy we began to build up the elevations, defining the pier sizes and revising the scheme in the normal to and fro manner until the juxtaposition of windows, balconies, chimneys and so on had all been brought into play to further enrich the scheme.

The builder for the project was David Hobson of J.C. Lillywhite. We had worked with David before and had a lot of respect for his building skills and his generally sympathetic attitude towards architecture. We had met him previously while working with Kathryn Findlay's office, Ushida Findlay, and had managed to depart as good friends.

The project proceeded relatively straightforwardly and the masonry solution was built with hardly a hitch. Some corruption of the concept did occur, with the odd piece of steel framing being introduced, but this was usually the result of needing to speed up construction

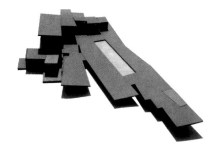

A simple card model by Toh Shimazaki explaining the house's spatial requirements in terms of its stratification in the landscape.

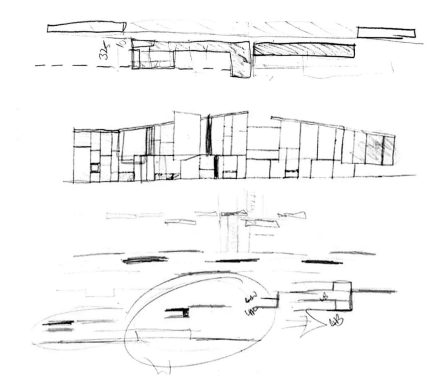

Preliminary engineering sketches considering the horizontal and vertical zoning of the external walls.

MASONRY

The main garden elevation
of the house as built, showing how the masonry piers
and areas of glazing merge
to create a balanced and
dynamic whole.

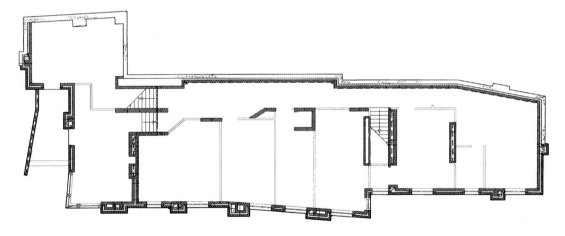

Plan of the lower ground
floor, dug into the site on
one side, showing the
perimeter load-bearing
masonry skin and piers.

A collage elevation by
Toh Shimazaki explor-
ing the colouring and
texture of the house and
its relationship to the
surrounding landscape.

on site and so did not distract from the overall strategy. Moreover, the architects had chosen a beautiful brick, Olde English Buff by Ibstock, which with its gentle pinkish hue complements perfectly the orangey-brown pale sand beds of East Grinstead. The finished building sits up well in the landscape and the brick narrative is very much apparent in the elevations.

Is it necessary for a material to tell its story in architectural terms, or is this just one approach to the creative process? I think the latter is probably the case, but the former is a good starting point. Either way, as an engineer I very much enjoy the muscularity of this building, which in its own way exemplifies the great qualities of masonry. In 2006, the OSH house was nominated by *World Architecture News* as one of the six best designed houses to have been completed in the world that year.

The house under construction, complete with its inward-sloping cantilevered roof and Iroko hardwood sunshades.

The house nestles into a spur of land at the top of the site, before the land falls away in a series of garden terraces.

A continuous plywood diaphragm beneath the insulation and metal roof finish provides much needed lateral stability to the perimeter walls.

A beautifully detailed wood and card model of the first floor showing the arrangement of the main living areas.

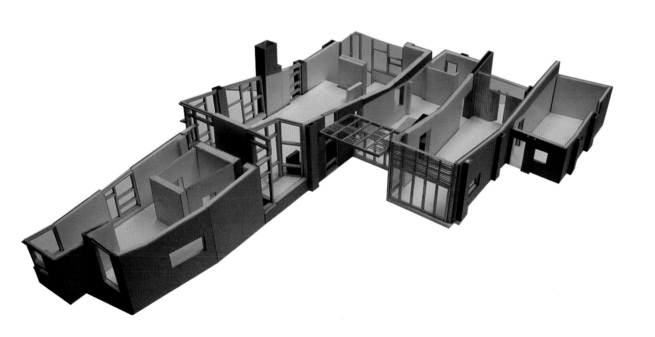

At the rear of the house, the kitchen and dining room areas open onto a terrace and pool.

The house is approached and entered at upper-ground level at one end, after which the site falls away on all three sides.

Steel

Steel

Steel is the king of ferric metals and when Henry Bessemer introduced the first inexpensive process for its mass production, it signalled the end of wrought iron as a construction material and accelerated the Industrial Age and the birth of the modern world.

Iron has been in use in Europe for thousands of years and is even mentioned in the Bible, as is steel (see Jeremiah 15:12). The Romans used it in their body armour and the Japanese were making beautiful swords in the material by the seventeenth century. Iron and steel have governed the emergence of European countries as world powers, ever since the forests of Germany and northern Italy first established themselves as the home of iron technology. The readily available iron ore in these areas, combined with carbon rich forests and fresh flowing rivers (for power and transport), drove the development of the Iron Age.

Iron can be broken down into the following three forms: cast iron, which is very strong and can be cast like silver or bronze, but cannot be worked; wrought iron, as used in the Eiffel

The Romans produced steel on a small scale to create weapons and armour.

Completed in 1890, the Firth of Forth rail bridge was the world's first major all-steel bridge.

Tower, which is easily bent and easily worked, because of its grain due to fibrous inclusions; and steel, which combines the best of both worlds. The major variable that gives each form its unique properties is due to their carbon content. In cast iron, the carbon content is high at approximately three per cent, allowing the material to flow readily. In wrought iron, the metal is worked and beaten reducing the carbon content to a bare minimum, while in steel the carbon content is around one per cent, creating a material which can be cast but is also strong and hard enough to retain an edge.

In 1855, Bessemer discovered that some pig iron ingots left in the hot air of a furnace had developed steel shells. At that time, adding air to a furnace was considered ridiculous as it was bound to cool the process. In the face of conventional thinking, Bessemer explored the idea and forced high pressure air into the furnace and through the molten iron. To his surprise

Introduced in the 1850s, the Bessemer converter allowed the mass production of good quality steel for the first time.

Perfected in the fifteenth century, the *katana* or long samurai sword is made up of a sophisticated layering of hard and soft steels.

he found that, because the air caused exothermic oxidation with the silicon and carbon 'impurities', it actually made the furnace hotter. The oxidation process also removed impurities such as silicon, manganese and, crucially, carbon as oxides. These escaped as gas or formed a solid slag.

Following Bessemer's discovery, steel quickly established itself as an important building material. Cheap steel facilitated the expansion of the railway and the construction of multi-storey skyscrapers. It changed the design of bridges and facilitated the construction of bigger ships. Steel also opened the doors for mechanisation and allowed the creation of much more powerful engines, gears and axles. In Scotland, the Forth Bridge was completed in 1890, with the use of 51,000 tonnes of steel. The Ritz Hotel in London (1904) and The Waldorf in New York (1908) were two of the early jewels of the new steel construction.

Rising 120 metres over the River Truyère in France, Gustave Eiffel's steel bridge of 1885 was for many years the tallest in the world.

Over the last 100 years, steel grades have changed and developed. Steel reinforcement has changed in the past 30 years from plain bars to ribbed bars to cold-twisted deformed bars and, most recently, to thermo-mechanically treated bars. And there will undoubtedly be more improvements as new grades of steel are introduced. Steel production has also grown massively in the past 100 years, from approximately 25 million tonnes at the start of the twentieth century to in excess of 800 million tonnes by its end. In short, the material has transformed the planet and the way we live and, if you include its use in reinforced concrete, it has become the primary material for creating our contemporary world.

Modern Steel and its Uses

Rod Arad said a funny thing about metals: 'I thought that you had to be a craftsman to make furniture and products in wood and ceramics. For some reason, I didn't think this extended to metals, so I started making things in metal instead.' For a structural engineer, too, steel is a very appealing material. It allows you to create 'skeletons' which encompass space, and it allows you to design the bones of these skeletons, the beams and columns, in a simple way. The jointing systems for steel elements are not complicated and usually offer a choice between bolts and welding. The mathematics to resolve the forces and to quantify the bolts or weld sizes are not rocket science either.

Adler and Sullivan's 1891 Wainwright Building in St Louis, the world's first steel-framed skyscraper.

Steel is also good in that it is a homogeneous material; it is not complicated in the way that you need to worry about the heterogeneous nature of reinforced concrete, say, with its deflections and possible cracking. A steel frame clearly resolves the forces within it, carrying the load on a floor to the columns and down to the foundations. Horizontal forces are quite often resolved by diagonal cross-bracing, which resolves the wind load into nice trigonometrical vectors. More than this, steelwork is often a happy marriage between the structural engineer's desire for a simple 'resolved forces' narrative and contemporary architecture's desire to move away from the load-bearing walls of the Beaux Arts tradition and embrace the freedom of the frame solution with its uninterrupted floor plates.

Returning to Ron Arad's words, it's true that steel is very forgiving. You can join it, polish it, work it and, most importantly, correct your mistakes with relative ease. With steel you can grind a piece off or weld a piece on, and then make good the surface finish as though nothing has ever been out of place. You can't do that easily with timber, glass or concrete. Steel is also the powerful material that allows you to push out to the extremes without breaking the budget. Its strength to depth ratio and its Young's modulus ($E=210,000$ N/m², stress/strain) make it a uniquely adaptable material, appropriate for the modern world.

However, despite all the bravado and machismo of the material on a great scale, another face is emerging that is also of interest. With laser-cutting techniques, core wrenching

Ron Arad's Europa sofa, fabricated entirely from polished stainless steel.

Designed with Richard Hyams' Astudio, this competition proposal for a bridge in Leicester included a perforated steel deck in honour of the area's lace-making heritage.

and biaxial bending, the rectilinear language of steel is being eroded and new 'softer' forms are being fabricated without exorbitant costs. These techniques are interesting because they allow a steel element to be made bespoke to its structural role, thereby avoiding the need to reach always for readily available pre-rolled section sizes. If a spanning beam requires its maximum depth mid-span, then we can use triangular shaped beams. If a steel plate does not need to be solid, then let's remove the superfluous material and let the light in. These new abilities to turn solids into meshes, to remove as well as add, are at last allowing steel to be more expressive in its structural role.

Royal Festival Hall Canopies

Having worked with Allies and Morrison on two previous projects, the bookcases for The Guardian Visitors' Centre and a glass cube art installation next to Tate Britain, we were very keen to escape the shackles of being perceived as engineers that worked only with glass. As a practice we are interested in exploring new materials, but we are just as keen to re-explore traditional materials and advance solutions where the chosen material is simply the best one for fulfilling the architectural intent.

Paul Appleton, an Allies and Morrison director, asked us if we would like to be involved in the design of the new entrance canopies for the Royal Festival Hall. They were a very small part of a multi-million pound project, but it was 'front of house' and needed to be carefully thought about. In the first few meetings we talked about the notion of entrances, the context of 1950s architecture, how we could address the river and the correct circulation strategy. The discussions were enlightening and we were happy to take part, bringing ideas to the table.

Allies and Morrison's presentation section through the Royal Festival Hall, including the river-front terrace and one of its two staircase canopies.

After several meetings we had the bare bones of a concept and had talked through the notion of what we were trying to achieve. We had considered whether the canopies were free-standing sculptures, scaled-up pieces of furniture or beacons on the river front and so on. This 'loose' approach concept-wise was a very healthy thing as it allowed all involved to put forward their own ideas in a spirit of goodwill, and then allowed parts of the different proposals to cross-fertilise and become elements of two or three different new ideas.

Reacting to these discussions, we went away and decided to make several different cardboard maquettes that explored the possible structural options. These were made up by cutting up old A4 paper boxes and gluing the pieces of cardboard together. First, we made

A view of one of the external staircases linking the upper terrace to the river, now crowned by an elegant steel canopy.

142

a base representing the two different concourse levels and then began to explore how the canopies might be supported on the two different levels. We made canopies with two, three and four columns, and with different combinations of columns and walls. A number of people in the office put forward ideas, including Ahmet Ucakan who came up with an asymmetrical two legs / one wall arrangement. I didn't think this would be acceptable, but we shoved them all into a big black plastic bag and took them to the next meeting. The architects responded well. They looked beyond the bad gluing, the printer's boxes, the creases and folds and saw something they liked in these 'knocked up' models, and were particularly taken with Ahmet's model.

This way of working keeps the looseness and allows the structural engineer, who often feels inarticulate in design conversations, to participate in the process. The maquettes

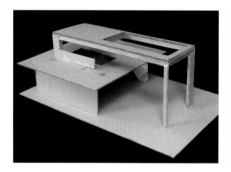 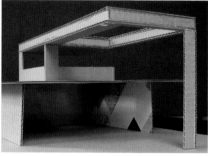 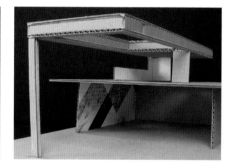

were not architectural models in the sense of showing how the completed design might look (these came later); instead, they were little three-dimensional representations of structural load paths that could also inspire the design dialogue.

After this process the solutions quickly became apparent. Ahmet's form was a success and now the more conventional aspect of the structural engineer's input could begin. We quickly decided that the canopies had to be steel. They had to span a long way. They had to be slim and elegant, and there is no current material in common use which can match steel's strength to depth ratio. Finite element analysis was undertaken, with the architects constantly pushing us to minimise the depth of the roof elements.

We decided that to achieve the slimmest possible construction, we would propose a 'waffle' plate steel scheme for the roof, not unlike double-hull ship construction. In this situation a 10mm thick steel plate was laid out, onto which were welded lines of ribs in both directions to create the waffle. A top sheet of steel, pierced by narrow slots that matched

Just three of the six rough cardboard models that were made to show the architects how the canopy might be supported.

Vmax Shear forces (kN/m)

0.0
0.4
0.8
1.2
1.6
2.0
2.4
2.8
3.2
3.6
4.0
4.4
4.8
5.2
5.6
6.0
6.4

A detailed finite element analysis was carried out to determine the stress topography of the entire structure.

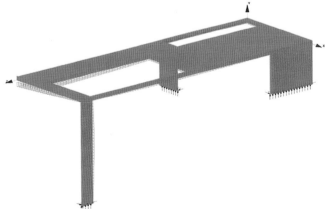

The structural principle of the canopy is that of a three-legged stool, albeit with legs sitting at different levels.

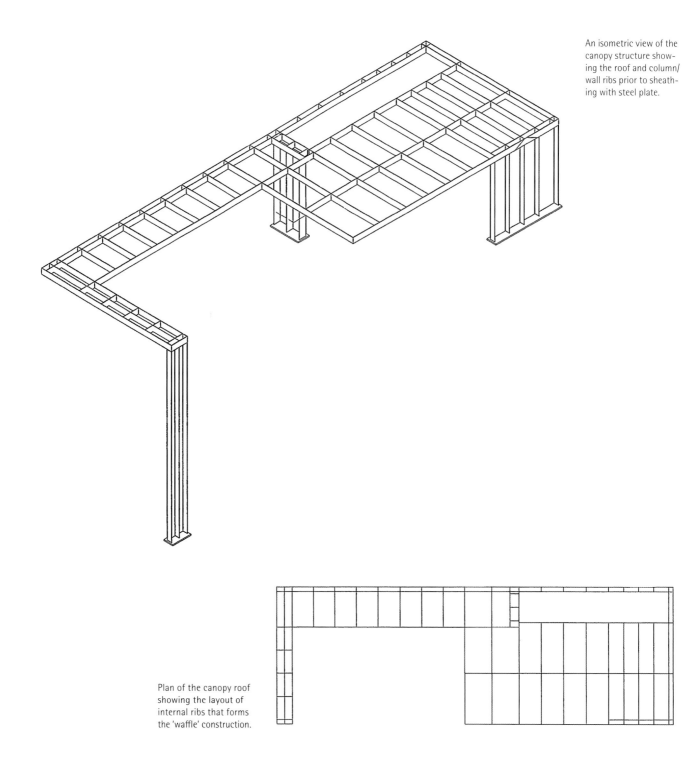

An isometric view of the canopy structure showing the roof and column/wall ribs prior to sheathing with steel plate.

Plan of the canopy roof showing the layout of internal ribs that forms the 'waffle' construction.

the size of the waffle, was then laid on top of the ribs and welded to them by plugging the holes with weld. In this way, a very strong composite sandwich was formed which allowed us to span 17 metres in a depth of 250mm.

When fabrication began, the work was initially sourced from a Malaysian shipyard. However, due to their nonchalant attitude towards the programme, it was decided to change subcontractors and go to Littlehampton Welding, a company with a very good track record in steel bridge fabrication. The canopies were made up in three sections to ease transportation to site. The different components were then erected and welded together to form the full three-dimensional structure, after which it was zinc sprayed on site and painted over.

The day before the props were removed was a very nervous one in the office. While the canopies were in essence three-legged stools, albeit with legs on different concourses, we could not relax. The fear was that when the props were removed, the canopy – which

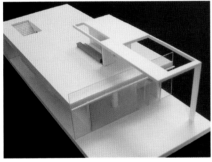
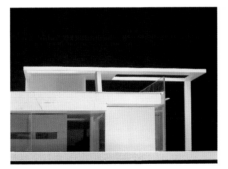
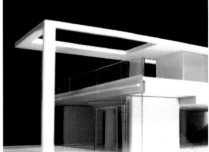

Allies and Morrison's 'architectural' model of the new canopy, complete with glazed elevations to the retail units at the lower level.

cantilevers some five metres – would deflect and sway in a scornful fashion. I remember coming back to the office that evening and re-running the computer analysis, then checking it by hand as a rough approximation. The thought of having to ring Paul to ask him if he would like an additional column filled me with dread. In a way, these instants are the engineer's moment of truth and they have to be faced as part of what we do. Everything we do sits under this moment and guides our approach, our cautiousness and challenges our desire to innovate.

Thankfully, there were no such problems and the canopies were successfully completed in the summer of 2006. The refurbished Royal Festival Hall has been an enormous success, and in 2008 it was nominated for the Stirling Prize.

The waffle ribs, stitch welded to the bottom sheet prior to location of the top layer of steel.

Each canopy was prefabricated in two sections to simplify delivery to site.

The canopies were fabricated by Littlehampton Welding who have considerable experience of pier and pontoon construction.

A view of the canopy during construction, showing the primary elements as they were being connected.

Removing the temporary construction props at the cantilevered corner was a major 'hold-your-breath' moment.

A view of the finished canopy showing two of its supports at the upper terrace level with the third reaching down to the river embankment.

A view of the renovated upper terrace, where the concrete barriers of old have been replaced by glass balustrades and the new canopies to create a vibrant public space.

The canopy floating above the new café and retail spaces at the river embankment level.

The power of the double cantilever is encapsulated in this photograph, where the corner of the roof appears to float.

ROYAL FESTIVAL HALL CANOPIES

Two Footbridges

These two footbridges are the only story in this book which illustrates an unfinished project, but I have decided to include it because I think it touches on the fundamentals of an engineer's role in the design process.

I'm not very good at drawing and I'm not very technical, not like a proper mathematically minded engineer who can peer deep into problems and distil solutions using analysis. I have ideas though, and I love engineering. I know where to pilfer from and quite often I know what has been done before by my peers. I respect engineers and the ones I really admire I seek out, befriend and accept their counsel – if they'll give it. There's a kind of inarticulateness that exists in structural engineering, which is a product of the educational system and people who are comfortable with numbers. There have been a few noble attempts to drag engineers more into the world of design inventiveness, while trying to ensure that their science and mathematical background is not diluted. However, drawing, communication, expressing and conveying ideas are not at the forefront of their education.

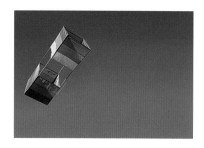

The simplest of structures, the box kite has inspired many a budding structural engineer.

For anyone wanting to know how things work, Airfix models and balsa wood kits provided the perfect introduction.

As a kid, I made things from cardboard boxes and later from Airfix and out of balsa. It was the usual motley collection of boats and aircraft, houses and forts. I also loved to make kites — the bigger, the better. I have worked in engineering offices in the UK, Europe and Africa, but I've also worked in architectural offices and, as previously mentioned, hung out in architecture schools for a long time.

The bridges came to us as a project from Stephen Richards of Gillespies, the urban and landscape designers based just off St John's Street in Farringdon. We had worked together previously on competitions, and had come close (in the last four) on a few occasions, but had never built anything together. These were a relatively humble prospect, two footbridges for shoppers spanning about 11 metres, to be installed in a huge new retail development by Hammerson in Sheffield. They needed to be built cheaply and preferably, as Stephen explained, somehow related but not the same.

The tower rising above Herzog & de Meuron's De Young Museum in San Francisco, a steel structure clad with perforated panels.

Ruth Asawa's filigree sculptures provide a masterclass for those seeking to understand the inherent possibilities of mesh structures.

The previous year, I had spent a short week with my daughter in San Francisco. We had been up to see the De Young Museum by Herzog & de Meuron and, while there, had noticed an exhibition of Ruth Asawa's work. She is a Japanese American sculptor who has spent most of her life working in mesh, evolving forms and perfecting her technique to create, using small, brilliant metal braids, natural organic forms with sensual curves and plant-like features. I was enthralled and amazed and could only imagine how this technique could be adopted in structural engineering. Just change the scale, I thought, and then there could be buildings, vessels and even bridges – perhaps two footbridges. This exhibition, coupled with our interest in mesh as a structural material, was the seed of our response to the Hammerson scheme.

When we met Gillespies, we talked about cutting away from the base material to allow light to percolate through the structure. Several meetings were held when it was just

The kitchen table on Friday night, complete with cardboard, scissors, Sellotape, coffee and daughter!

enough to talk about the idea without drawings, without analysis, just sowing the seeds. The architects responded by teasing out the notion of a footbridge consisting of laths and spars, not worrying about how we might address the structural concerns. This evolutionary work helped them to explore their own ideas, but we needed to participate more. Being afraid to start drawing and being uncomfortable that what was in our mind's eye could not be conveyed, we resorted to the old trick of making 'knocked-up' models. I call them 'knocked up' because that's important – the looser or less precious they are, the more freely they can be interpreted.

On a Friday evening, I sat down and set to work with old business cards and brochures, Sellotape and a pair of blunt scissors. The bridges would be a simple exploration of how to span across a gap, and the structural premise was to provide 'meat' where strength was needed, but to cut away at the elements where it was less critical. The relationship between the two bridges would be taken care of by their geometry, their similar material and their compatible spans. The bridges also needed to address their support conditions and be compatible with the retail style balustrades at each end.

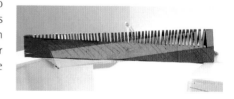

A model of Bridge One with its inclined beams shown shaded in different colours.

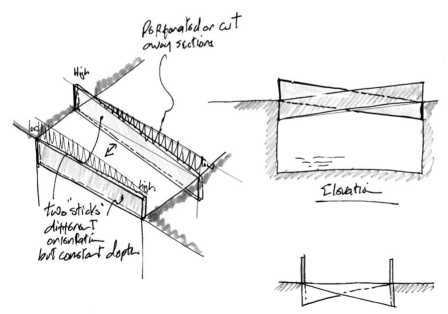

An early sketch of the first bridge, seeking to work out the structural logic of its two opposing inclined beams.

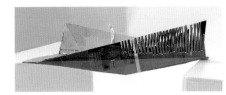

A rough cardboard model of Bridge Two, showing the structural 'meat' of the beams shaded in green.

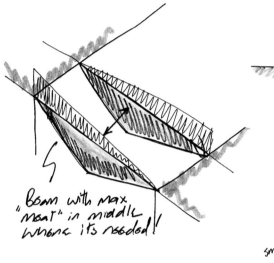

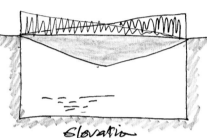

An early sketch of the second bridge, setting out its structural logic and exploring its relationship with the other bridge.

"Beam with max "meat" in middle where its needed!

Slevation

small getting bigger

By getting smaller

A number of simple card maquettes were made to fully examine the three-dimensional qualities of both bridges.

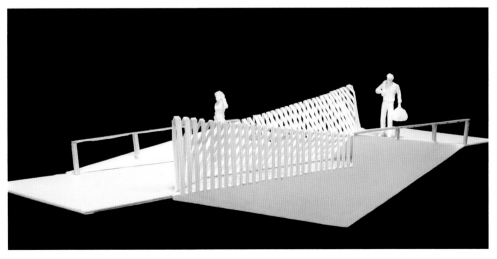

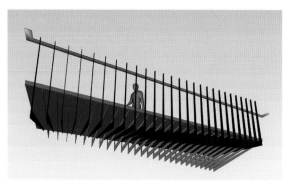

Gillespies prepared their own computer images to help them understand the structural geometry of the two bridges.

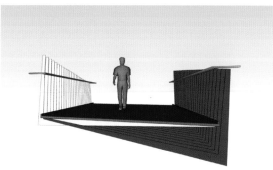

Gillespies' end-on view of Bridge One showing how the structural ribs could be extended to form the balustrades.

Gillespies' drawing of Bridge One managed to capture the general shape of the bridge, if not always its structural integrity.

Model people were incor-
porated into the models
(here of Bridge One) to
establish a true sense of
scale.

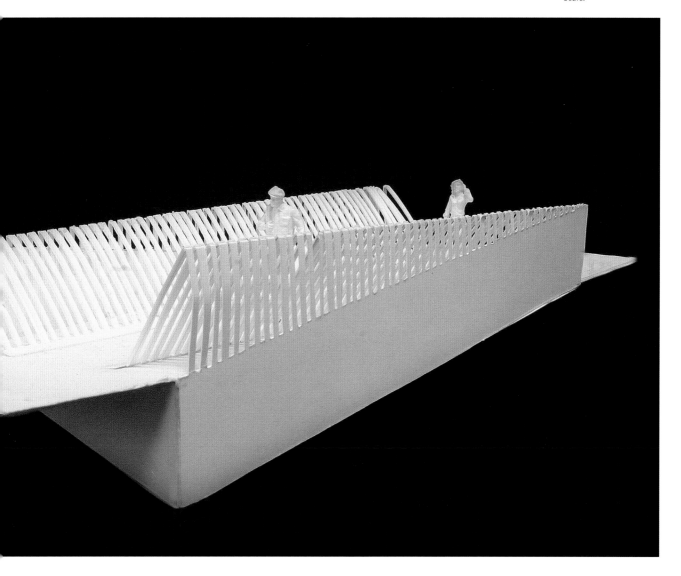

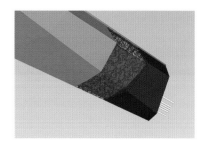

An early Gillespie image exploring the possibility of incorporating a perforated 'skin' to line the bridge's underside and balustrades.

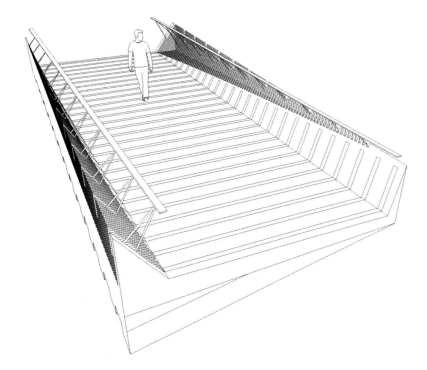

A perspective drawing of Bridge One in its final form, with its structural and architectural ideas fully harmonised.

Bridge One, the brother, was simple: beams on either side of the bridge were orientated diagonally, but set against each other and then connected to the deck. In contrast, Bridge Two, the sister, would have beams but triangular ones with the maximum depth (or meat) in the middle of the span. When complete, the maquettes were suitably ugly and clumsy, but appropriate for the next meeting. We photographed them in black and white, not realising that the power of the idea was captured in these simple photographs, going a long way in helping the architects to hear our 'voice' more articulately. For once, the structural ideas and design aesthetic were deeply intertwined and this enriched the presentation, which was enthusiastically received by the client.

The point of all this is that engineers must not be afraid to express their ideas and, more importantly, they need to reach out to find a way to articulate what is inside them. Architects have to do this as a fundamental part of their job, but they don't always have the depth of knowledge required to instil an idea with the richness of structural understanding. It is always best if both sides can work together on equal terms.

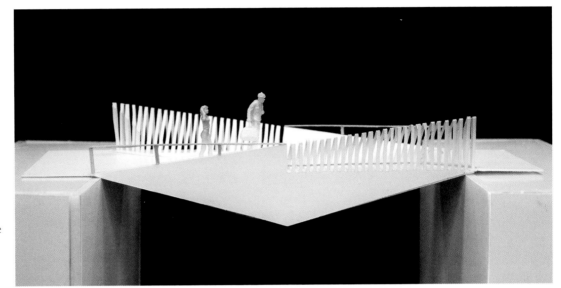

A card model of 'female' Bridge Two, made by Luke Gardner at Fluid, exploring an alternative option for the handrail.

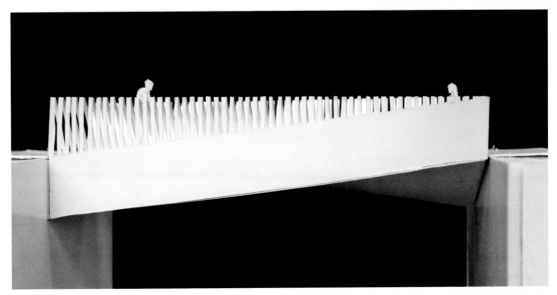

Luke Gardner's model of the 'male' Bridge One, showing the visual twist created by the structure on its underside.

The Victoria Miro Gallery

The Victoria Miro Gallery is a private art space off Old Street in east London. When the project was first outlined by the client, Warren Miro, he asked if it would be possible to construct a new floor on top of his existing building in Wharf Road. Initial research confirmed that the building had been constructed as a warehouse in the early twentieth century and, comparing its historic load capacity with the envisaged usage, we felt confident that an additional floor would not be a problem. Little did we appreciate that the additional floor would be almost seven metres tall, or that Warren was setting out to achieve the foremost art space in London, easily eclipsing any rivals in nearby Hoxton Square.

The architect for the new scheme was Claudio Silvestrin, the internationally acclaimed maestro of Minimalism. We had worked with him previously and knew that he would ferociously guard his proposals and would not accept any compromise — well maybe a tiny bit. In the beginning, the scheme seemed dreamlike, a beautiful white box perched on top of the gritty, squat warehouse and cantilevering with a sensual curve above the streetscape. It

was an exciting project, unlike anything we had built before, but we were relaxed. Claudio's drawings were beautiful, conceptual and elegant but, in our view, the planners at Hackney Council would surely take a dim view. There seemed little point, therefore, in crossing too many bridges at this stage, though when the client fretted whether the scheme could be built, I was happy to reassure him that if he ever got planning permission, then we would be able to engineer it.

Easy words with such a prequalification. The client asked us for precedents and delightfully paid us a small fee to prepare a study. We looked into all the white boxes we could find from the last 20 years, including Michael Manser's Heathrow Hilton Hotel and Conran's Bluebird Café, indeed, any lightweight steel box regardless of the type of white cladding. We showed him Richard Meier's work and Claudio nodded ... as if to say yes, maybe that kind of thing, but obviously much better!

Claudio Silvestrin's design sections through the building, showing the new extension at roof level and the dramatic 'single-run' staircase leading up to it.

160

Elevation showing the new gallery and its open-sided courtyard perched on top of the existing warehouse building.

The new rooftop gallery as seen from City Road, with its smooth white rendered elevations and high level external court-yard.

Claudio Silvestrin's original design elevations show the cantilevered gallery clad with white metal panels, not ren-der, but is accurate in all other details.

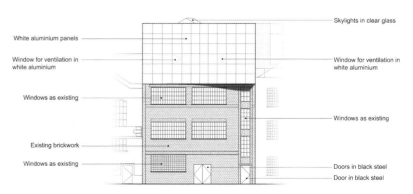

White aluminium panels

Window for ventilation in white aluminium

Windows as existing

Existing brickwork

Windows as existing

Skylights in clear glass

Window for ventilation in white aluminium

Windows as existing

Doors in black steel

Door in black steel

The key to the project was to build the new rooftop extension in steel and timber, and clad it in lightweight materials. Steel allowed us to span the full width of the building without intermediate support, but was light enough to avoid the need to build new foundations or to underpin the existing walls. Finally, news came through that the planners liked the scheme and that an arts quarter fitted perfectly well with their plans for the locality. With this endorsement and with the help of an executive architect, the project proceeded at a pace to tender.

The client was seduced into awarding the contract, on a construction management basis, to a well-known London contractor with good experience of this type of work. Needless to say, the client believed that great management would save lots of time and would leave him free to finalise parts of the design during the early stages of construction. Unfortunately, the contract became a disaster pretty soon after it started. The existing building surveys were all contradictory, leaving the executive architect to swerve from pillar to post as he tried to set out the new elements of the building based on the conflicting information. Four months into the project and we were already more than 12 weeks behind schedule. Drastic action was required and, after several high level meetings, it was agreed to bring in a project manager to try to sort out the problems and reschedule the works.

It had been decided that a tower crane was not necessary for the project (not our advice) and that a temporary roof with travelling gantry crane would be sufficient for erecting the steelwork once it had been raised to the existing roof level by hoist. To facilitate this construction technique, the project engineer John Graham designed the main steel beams to be spliced at approximately five-metre centres. Because the new roof was to be architecturally flat — drained solely by creating falls in the insulation — the joints had to be full moment

The ground- and new top-floor plans, showing the staircase zone running along the angled wall and the new lift, located at the rear of the building with its own access.

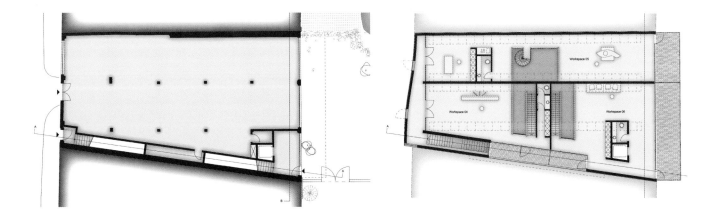

Two of the computer renderings of the proposed scheme that were submitted as part of the planning application.

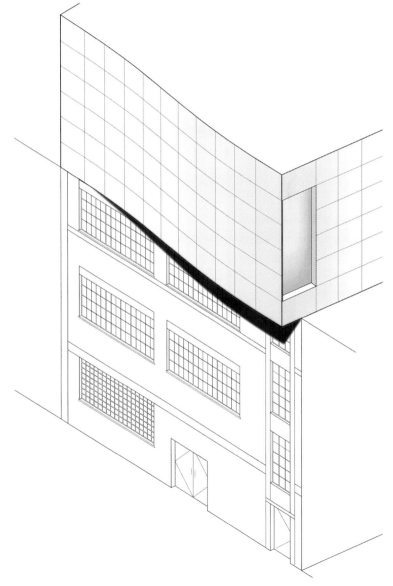

Claudio Silvestrin's isometric view of the extension, complete with the curved profile of the cantilever as built as well as the tall side window that illuminates the top of the long stairs.

THE VICTORIA MIRO GALLERY

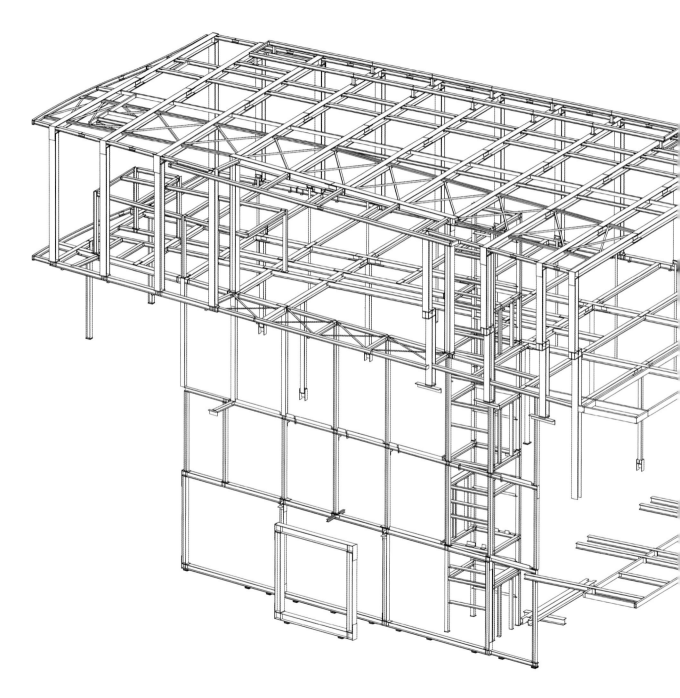

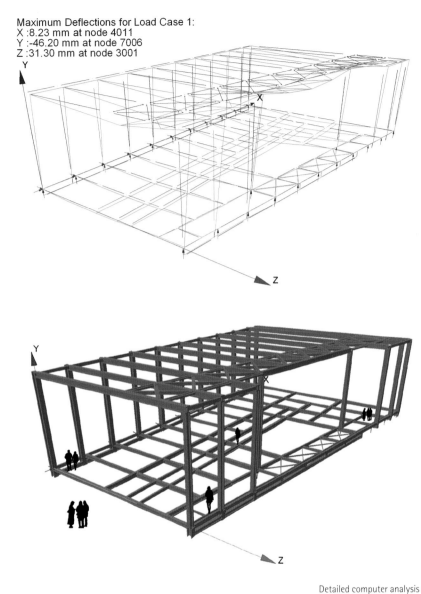

Maximum Deflections for Load Case 1:
X :8.23 mm at node 4011
Y :-46.20 mm at node 7006
Z :31.30 mm at node 3001

Detailed computer analysis models were prepared by Fluid Structures to determine the best sizes for the main structural members in resisting wind loadings and deflections due to the long span of the roof.

A fabrication drawing of all the new steelwork as prepared by Bourne Special Projects. Apart from the gallery, new steel was needed to support the wall alongside the long staircase as well as a new liftshaft and balcony at the rear of the building.

The rooftop space is broken down into three main galleries, lined in plasterboard and separated by lightweight studwork.

The rooftop gallery's new floor, shown here under construction in white-painted steel-work.

An internal view of the double-height gallery as the main steel frame nears completion, while installation of the partial mezzanine floor continues.

The warehouse's original saw-tooth roof before its demolition to make way for the new gallery.

connections, so we specified high strength friction-grip bolts to ensure the connection plates would be clamped securely to the steel sections. These were installed, but incorrectly, causing the roof steels to sag. The steel subcontractor whinged that the beams were not man enough for the job, and only when we insisted on checking the torque in the bolts did we confirm that they had not been tightened properly.

The original structural concept was further challenged by Claudio's new main staircase, which rose from ground level to the third floor as a single continuous flight with scant regard for its tortured context. We had initially expected this to be a scissors stair, neatly dropped into a void at each floor level, but he would have none of that. The stair had to rise continuously, as though from hell to heaven. Much to our surprise, by fiddling with the landing dimensions, this proved to be acceptable and within the Building Regulations. Thus, the stair cut a massive slot through the building, which of course removed support for the slab alongside it at each floor level. There was no alternative but to install a new wall, made from steel beams and

Detail views of the steel frame, including a close-up of the central splice in the main roof beam (above), steel cross-bracing (centre), and the cantilevered steel-work for the rear balcony (far right).

columns, descending through the building to the ground floor, where we were finally dragged into the area of new foundation works.

The project proved to be remarkably challenging and brought home the difficulties of carrying out open-heart surgery on an existing building. The predominant lesson learnt was that it's far better to get as much of the information finalised and documented before starting on site. In addition, the issues of construction tolerances, setting out and knowledge of the existing building should never be underestimated. I often pass close to the Victoria Miro Gallery on my travels around London and can never resist going to have another peep. The work is very unusual for London and we're still very proud to have acted as Claudio's engineers. It defies many of the things we hear architecturally about scale and context, yet somehow it is more powerful and successful for it.

A view of the finished gallery from Wharf Road, with its large lancet window at the top of the stairs and white rendering over the lightweight support structure.

An overall view of the gallery as seen from the junction of Wharf Road and Micawber Street.

The double-height space of the completed gallery and two views of the vertiginous long staircase leading from the ground-floor entrance to the rooftop gallery.

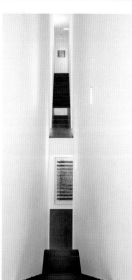

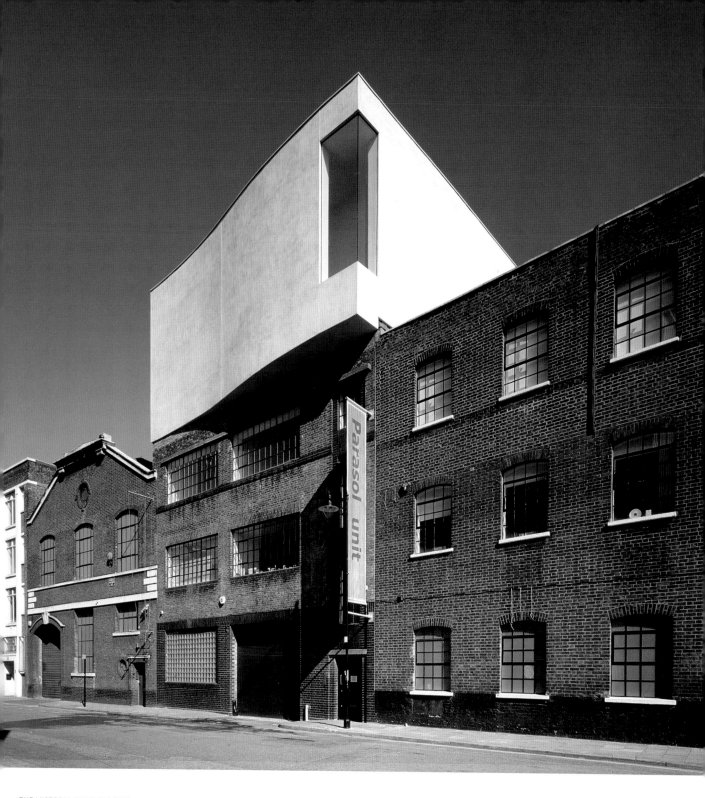

Stanley Gardens Staircase

Stanley Gardens was the first project that brought us together with Make Architects. It was not what we had initially expected, as the project turned out to be the refurbishment of a five-storey listed property in west London. But this didn't matter; we were excited to be working with them as we knew that they were a hothouse of talent. Their openness, design-wise, was refreshing and they seemed to embrace an office culture that allowed new ideas and people into their adventure.

The project was small for them and perhaps relatively unknown territory. Still, they set about it with lots of enthusiasm and creative thought. The property lies in the jurisdiction of a well-known local conservation officer in the borough of Kensington and Chelsea, and we had worked on a number of projects on her patch. We knew that, structurally, we would not be doing too much and that the historic fabric would need to be maintained, as would the majority of the original internal layout — normally quite a contentious issue. We bided our time while the project architects Christina Gresser and later Christina Leung decoded the

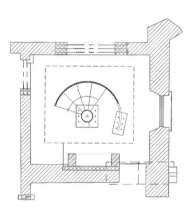 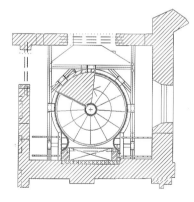

Fluid Structures' plans of the lower and upper ground floors (far left and left), showing the supplementary beams required around the latter's floor opening.

possibilities of what might be acceptable, appeasing the conservationists while supporting their client's desire to create a contemporary family home. Our work settled down to inserting a few new openings (with steel box frames), repairs to the roof and guidance on the removal of cracks, all carried out under the normal gambit required for a conservation project of minimal intervention and sympathetic techniques.

The key move in terms of circulation was to introduce a new staircase which would link the lower ground floor with the entrance level to the house. The original stone staircase had been tampered with and no longer served the lower floor area. After considering the options, it was decided to remedy this with a spiral stair, even though this would clearly be a contemporary

An elevational view of the stair, with its oak treads and handrails offset by a beautifully clear low-iron glass balustrade.

Preliminary computer renderings prepared by Make to explore the overall size and position of the proposed spiral staircase.

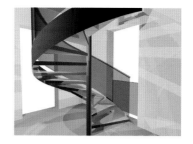 

Plans of the ground floor *(above left)* showing the top of the spiral stair opening off the kitchen, and the first floor *(above)* with the oculus in the study next to the sitting room.

The lower ground floor plan showing the bottom of the spiral stair adjacent to the family and wine-tasting rooms.

Make's computer rendering showing how the stair links the upper and lower ground floors.

insertion within the historic fabric. The spiral solution, however, did avoid the need to knock down walls (which a straight flight would have required), while subtly subverting the historic tradition of a clear separation between family and servant quarters. It also afforded the opportunity to embellish the house with a special moment and add the signature of the new owner.

As the design of the stair developed and the concerns for its size within the space dissipated, it was decided that the inner string should consist of a steel sheet curved to the required profile, thereby also acting as a spine support. This gave the stair a more fluid profile than a central post and accentuated its graceful sinusoidal curved form. To heighten the contrast between the solid horizontal treads and this new twisted element, the helically rolled steel plate would be 'dematerialised' by cutting holes into it – although leaving sufficient material to support the treads and risers. This was done using a CNC machine, programmed to cut out the selected patterns. To soften the apertures, they were hand finished before the steel spine was hot-metal sprayed with copper, then acid patinated and sealed with wax.

Both Make and Fluid made models to examine all the design parameters necessary to ensure the top and bottom of the stair were in the best position.

This technique of perforating primary steel elements was also used to create a cylinder at first floor level that acts as protection to a glass oculus, which was inserted in the first floor directly above the stair. The oculus allows light to penetrate the lower floors, while also retaining a memory of the original ceiling rose (which had been damaged), its form having been etched into the glass. With its piercings and copper finish, the cold sheet steel has been transformed into a rich, modern lattice-like material which sits comfortably in a landscape of bespoke walnut fittings and low iron glass. This willingness to embrace the very latest technologies and techniques, including CNC cutting techniques, computer-generated patterns and the Rhino modelling, is very much a signature of our times. These new processes break our historical understanding of materials and allow us to re-examine our perceptions about their design.

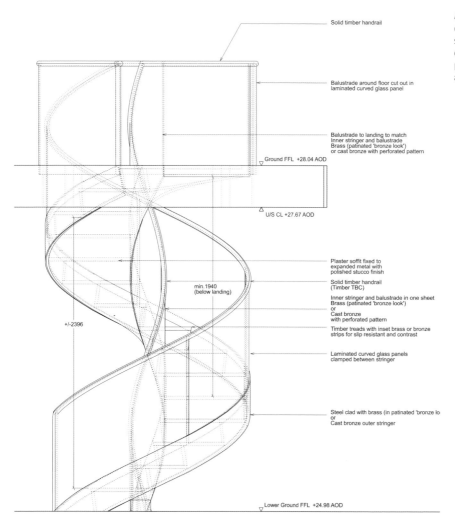

Solid timber handrail

Balustrade around floor cut out in
laminated curved glass panel

Balustrade to landing to match
Inner stringer and balustrade
Brass (patinated 'bronze look')
or cast bronze with perforated pattern

▽ Ground FFL +28.04 AOD

△ U/S CL +27.67 AOD

Plaster soffit fixed to
expanded metal with
polished stucco finish

Solid timber handrail
(Timber TBC)

Inner stringer and balustrade in one sheet
Brass (patinated 'bronze look')
or
Cast bronze
with perforated pattern

Timber treads with inset brass or bronze
strips for slip resistant and contrast

min.1940
(below landing)

Laminated curved glass panels
clamped between stringer

+/-2396

Steel clad with brass (in patinated 'bronze lo
or
Cast bronze outer stringer

▽ Lower Ground FFL +24.98 AOD

Architectural elevation
of the stair showing the
sinusoidal form of the
central support and the
positioning of the wrap-
around treads and risers.

A 3D view of the stair
showing the outer glass
balustrade and its con-
tinuous oak handrail.

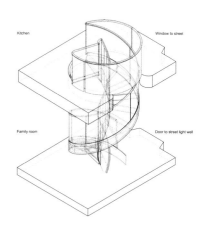

The initial design was developed and fine-tuned by Millimetre Ltd, who then prefabricated the whole stair in their workshop in Brighton. They are a thoroughly modern company,
blending computer techniques and skills with craftsmanship and fabrication knowledge to
deliver bespoke one-offs. Apart from their fundamental workshop skills, their input and their
knowledge of finishes, aesthetics and beauty were to prove invaluable.

Martin Day of Day Building was the general contractor and, as usual, he delivered the
house to a very high standard of finish. The stair was delivered to site in three pieces and then
installed over a two week period. Any concerns about the installation proved unfounded and,
in fact, our main worry as engineers was how the Victorian floor joists would cope with the
sheer weight of a 50mm-thick glass oculus.

Finally I should mention the convex soffit of the stair, which is a very beautiful affair. It
is simply a polished plaster 'belly' over a timber lattice fixed to the steel strings that, despite
their manipulation and dematerialisation, have enough stiffness and strength not to wobble.

The perforated central support and the matching perforated cylinder that forms the balustrade around the glass oculus.

The complete spiral stair was prefabricated and preassembled in Millimetre's workshop, then disassembled for transport to site.

The design of the stair was fine tuned by Millimetre and their own engineering consultant at Hardman Structural Engineers.

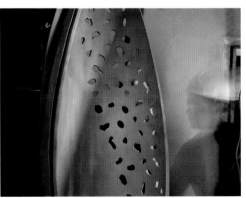

Detail views of the spiral staircase during its test assembly in Millimetre's workshop in Brighton.

Looking up the stair from the lower ground floor, with the acid-etched glass oculus set into the first floor visible above.

STEEL

The stair's perforated central support continues up to form the end of the cantilever balustrade.

A close-up view of the perforations in the central support *(below)* and looking down the staircase towards the lower-ground floor *(bottom)*, with its stone motif by the Swiss artist Karim Noureldin.

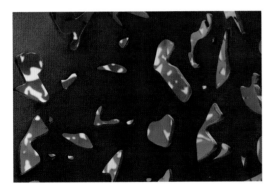

The glass oculus at first-floor level is protected by a perforated steel drum which also acts as a piece of bespoke furniture.

Timber

Timber

When I started working as a structural engineer, in 1984, timber was not part of the palette of materials that were studied or considered seriously. Concrete and steel were the real deal and timber was a lesser form, confined to floor joists or sacrificial shuttering for concrete work. Yes, you could buy timber products and specify gang nail roof trusses, but it did not really require engineering input. They were simply elements available in the market and structural engineers did not spend too much time querying this hierarchy.

In truth, consciousness about environmental issues was pretty low and we never stopped to consider the embodied energy of materials. Modernism was an international language with global solutions. Architectural and engineering considerations were resolved by new materials, technology and ideas imported from allied industries. We were interested in prefabrication and fast tracking. The consideration that an approach sensitive to the local context might be a more responsible attitude never occurred to us and we progressed merrily with our machines for living in and our homages to Mies van der Rohe, with their floor-to-floor glazing and full air conditioning. Things have changed a lot in the last 25 years and the fallacy of one style suits all has finally been laid to rest.

In the United Kingdom, timber was the predominant building material well into the seventeenth century, but the depletion of the indigenous forests and the rapid growth of towns was making the situation increasingly untenable. The Great Fire of London in 1666 demonstrated the folly of timber-framed construction in cities and, shortly afterwards, legislation limiting the use of timber as a primary building material was introduced to avoid further calamity. However, the legacy of the great periods of timber construction is all around us, and wood – notably oak – is a part of the country's prized heritage.

Built in the thirteenth century by the Knights Templar, the great barns at Cressing in Essex, with their unadorned oak structures, are stunningly sophisticated agricultural buildings. Three hundred years later, the construction of England's then finest warship, the *Mary Rose*, reputedly required the felling of in excess of 600 large oak trees gathered from all over southern England. Even at that time, mature oak was becoming a precious commodity and, for a seafaring nation with great skills in the working of wood, its continuing decline – both as a sustainable resource and in usage – was a cause for great concern and perhaps a depressing sign of things to come.

In more recent times, attention in the UK has refocused on the use of wood, both in terms of imported timber and the growth of native supplies. The Timber Research and Development Association (TRADA) was set up in 1934 to carry out government-funded research into the use of wood in the construction industry and, in its 75 years, it has been instrumental in promoting the use of wood and providing technical advice to designers and specifiers. TRADA has also led the way in pushing the boundaries of timber construction in

The sophistication of timber construction in the Middle Ages was truly remarkable, as the great oak-framed barn at Cressing illustrates.

Commissioned in 1393 and spanning 20.7 metres, the hammer-beam roof over the Great Hall of Westminster is the largest medieval roof ever built.

As *HMS Victory* demonstrates, oak remained the timber of choice for building ships right up until the early 1800s.

Completed in 1511 and lost in 1545, the *Mary Rose* reputedly used 600 mature oak trees in its construction.

Rachel Sandbrook of Fluid Structures explores the wonderfully tactile contents of the TRADA timber sample box.

the UK, playing a significant role in the development of multi-storey timber frame construction. The case for using timber as a primary structural material becomes more attractive each year, the more so because latest figures show that the size of Europe's forests are actually increasing, gaining an area about the size of Ireland every decade.

Things about the Material We Like

During Fluid's early years as a small practice, we were mostly confined to the refurbishment of existing buildings and houses in London, and timber projects were scarce. However, we were keen to use the material and build up our knowledge about the different types of wood and their sustainability for various usages. One of the first things we did was to join TRADA and, having become members, we sent away for their timber sample box.

This box contained some 30 different samples of wood from all over the world! They varied from the African hardwood idigbo to Asian lavan and from European sycamore to South American mahogany. It was a treasure trove that we still use and cherish. It allows you to touch the wood, check its weight and inspect its colouring and grain. It brings home the uniqueness of the material in terms of its accessibility and user friendliness. It defies you to not want to pick it up and start making things.

El Ray Beach House

I know that Simon Conder is one of the most talented architects I have ever worked with. His built projects are beautiful and, irrespective of budget, he reaches out as though each building is his last, marking out a career with a mesmeric devotion to craftsmanship and detail. I'm not saying he is an easy man to work with and we have had our spats over the years, but we have also built up a strong working relationship. He's strong willed but needs support. There's a price to be paid for creating beautiful things which sometimes extends beyond professionalism. It often crosses over into the world of commitment, friendship and patronage, and can involve services well beyond the call of duty and certainly outside the standard terms of an engineering contract.

We were asked by Simon to act as structural engineers for a new beach house to be located at El Ray in Dungeness. This is the site of one of his previous projects, the Black Rubber Beach House, which was the winner of numerous commendations, including an RIBA award and another from the American Institute of Architects. It's also a very English place,

The beach house under construction on the beach at Dungeness, in sight of the lighthouse and the power station.

not far from the site of the late Derek Jarman's garden, a place of beauty and desolation imbued with memories and an evocation of an England that seems forever rooted in the 1950s and '60s.

The brief was simple enough: a new single-storey beach house which would involve the retention of an old tram car that had previously served the area. The beach house is only accessible via a track that crosses an expanse of the beach itself, and for that as well as other economic reasons, we chose to build the beach house in lightweight and technologically simple materials. This complemented Simon's desire to clad the building in vertical hardwood boarding, which lent itself well to effecting the curved plan that was Simon's chosen form. The easiest way to build walls that curve on plan regularly involves timber or masonry. The

Approaching from landside via a gentle timber ramp, the vertical Itauba boards that clad the building seem an obvious choice for this most natural of environments.

The moment connections in the Kerto frame were made using Timberlok fasteners.

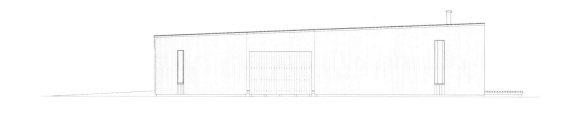

Simon Conder Associates' drawings of an elevation and section through the beach house, the latter indicating the location of the raft foundations and the retained tram car.

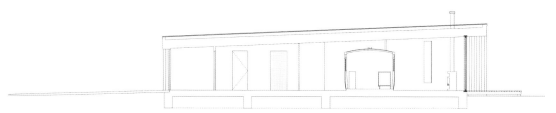

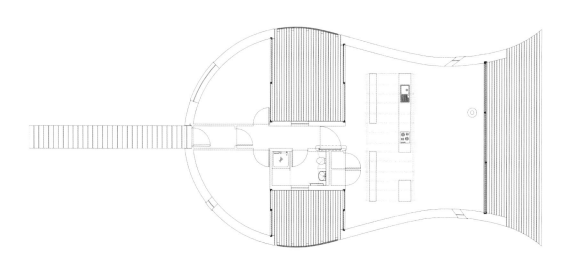

The plan of the beach house showing the two bedrooms at the rear, overlooking the concealed inner courtyards, and the kitchen/living quarters at the front.

nature of timber construction, with vertical studs at 400 to 600mm centres, allows you to move away from straight lines. And the same is true for masonry, where the 215mm or 440mm basic brick or block dimension allows you to articulate the line of the construction. It seems to me that both these are preferable to reinforced concrete, where the issue of bending reinforcement and installing specialist curved shuttering only serve to drive costs up.

The beach house is constructed completely in timber. For the walls we used Masonite studs, while Steico timber beams support the roof. A German engineered timber product, Steico was easily capable of spanning the eight or nine metres required on this project, yet was light enough to be positioned on site by one man without the use of mechanical lifting equipment.

At the front of the beach house, where it looks out towards the sea, there is a clear opening seven metres wide that contains top-hung folding sliding doors. This is a key feature of the design and we were concerned that any movement in the structure surrounding the opening might cause the doors to jam. This had to be avoided. We were initially tempted to

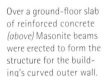

Over a ground-floor slab of reinforced concrete *(above)* Masonite beams were erected to form the structure for the building's curved outer wall.

introduce a steel portal frame, knowing that steel would provide the required rigidity. However, the introduction of such a foreign element into an otherwise all-timber composition seemed inappropriate. In addition, the use of steel would have required the temporary use of a mobile crane or, at best, a couple of lifting genies with some scaffolding and block and tackle to manoeuvre it.

Alternative solutions were considered, but in the end we elected to construct the portal frames using 'Kerto', a pre-engineered material made up of graded 3mm-thick laminated softwood veneers glued together. In designing the connection between beam and column we realised that the forces were too high for a single element made of this material, so simply doubled the number of frames. We also used a very interesting and relatively new timber fastener called Timberlok, which made the connections straightforward and thus far easier

A double Kerto portal frame was erected at the front of the house to provide lateral stability for the sliding doors.

for a non-specialist contractor to construct. This is another of the benefits of working with timber: it can be easily adapted and the skills required to erect it can be built up relatively quickly compared with materials such as steel or concrete.

The beach house was clad with shiplapped Itauba planks, which were secured to battens fixed directly back to the timber flanges of the Masonite studs. A breather membrane between the battens and studs provides secondary waterproofing during bad weather, while the building is insulated with blown cellulose fibre insulation located between the studs. Completed in 2008, the beach house went on to win the 2009 Stephen Lawrence Prize.

A plan view detailing the construction of the external wall, with its Masonite studwork, insulation and Itauba weatherboarding.

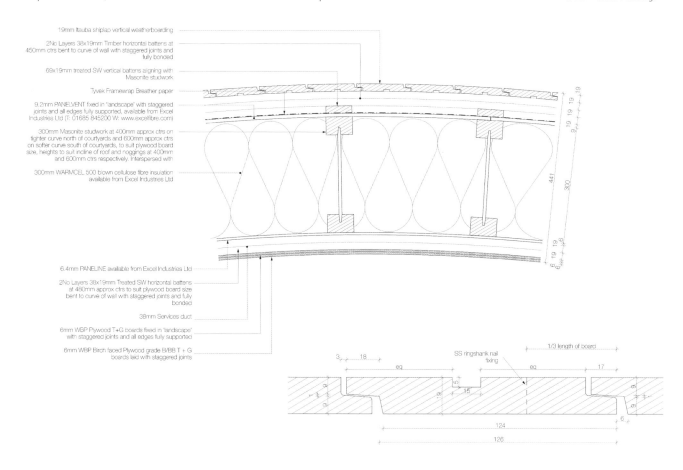

19mm Itauba shiplap vertical weatherboarding

2No Layers 38x19mm Timber horizontal battens at 450mm ctrs bent to curve of wall with staggered joints and fully bonded

69x19mm treated SW vertical battens aligning with Masonite studwork

Tyvek Framewrap Breather paper

9.2mm PANELVENT fixed in 'landscape' with staggered joints and all edges fully supported, available from Excel Industries Ltd (T: 01685 845200 W: www.excelfibre.com)

300mm Masonite studwork at 400mm approx ctrs on tighter curve north of courtyards and 600mm approx ctrs on softer curve south of courtyards, to suit plywood board size, heights to suit incline of roof and noggings at 400mm and 600mm ctrs respectively. Interspersed with

300mm WARMCEL 500 blown cellulose fibre insulation available from Excel Industries Ltd

6.4mm PANELINE available from Excel Industries Ltd

2No Layers 38x19mm Treated SW horizontal battens at 480mm approx ctrs to suit plywood board size bent to curve of wall with staggered joints and fully bonded

38mm Services duct

6mm WBP Plywood T+G boards fixed in 'landscape' with staggered joints and all edges fully supported

6mm WBP Birch faced Plywood grade B/BB T + G boards laid with staggered joints

1/3 length of board

SS ringshank nail fixing

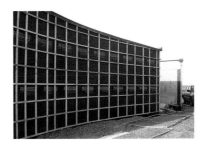

The shiplapped Itauba boards were fixed back to a framework of soft-wood battens over a layer of Tyvek Frame-wrap breather paper.

Details of the setting out for the Timberlok fasteners that create a moment connection between a Kerto beam and post.

9 NO. 14" LONG FASTENMASTER TIMBERLOK SCREWS FIXED EACH SIDE OF BEAMS TOP & BOTTOM AS SHOWN.

2 NO. 400x90 KERTO S BEAM

60   60   60   60

30 30

280   400

30 30

9 NO. 14" LONG FASTENMASTER TIMBERLOK SCREWS FIXED EACH SIDE OF BEAMS TOP & BOTTOM AS SHOWN.

4 NO. 240x45 KERTO S BEAMS

240

A layer of Panelvent boarding to the walls and marine ply on the roof provides rigidity against the high wind loads associated with the beach location.

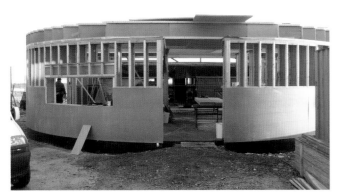

The finished El Ray beach house with its full-height glazed doors retracted to reveal a simple living area dominated by the salvaged tram car that forms the kitchen.

Itauba boards also line the roof deck which is fixed down on joists via adjustable feet over an EPDM waterproof membrane.

Looking out from inside the beach house, over the external deck to the sea. The internal walls and floor are lined in birch-faced plywood.

Tide and Times

The strange blobby timber structure that is the Tide and Times temporary pavilion was the result of a limited competition won by Alex Mowat's office, Urban Salon, in 2008. When Alex first approached us to become involved, he merrily informed us that the budget was minuscule, the fees practically nonexistent and that the whole thing had to be done in a bloody hurry. It's a testament to his determination, coupled with an adventurous design sensibility, that it got done at all, and I have to say that we did not bring that much to the party. We ran some early numbers only to realise that it would need weeks of computer analysis, but we did recommend timber specialist Gordon Cowley, because we knew he couldn't resist a challenge.

The structure of the pavilion consists of plywood 'ribbons', woven together to create a simple enclosure in the form of a large basket. While we were muttering about analysis, Alex decided to make a large section of the structure in his office to see what would happen. Aided and abetted by project architect Ray Cheung, they found some of the most awful 4mm plywood (Malaysian I think) and set about building it. Every time a section broke they knew it

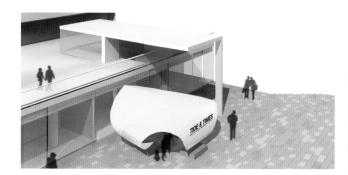

Urban Salon's first computer models defined a possible form for the pavilion, but at this stage not the structure.

was over-stressed and so glued on another piece of 4mm ply. While not structurally conventional, it was certainly an active approach that helped drive the design process. Making 'stuff' like this opens up new avenues, shows how it might be done differently and allows you to really immerse yourself in the three-dimensional geometry of a problem — a healthy alternative to digital models that can only be explored on two-dimensional screens.

Alex's primitive prototype showed up a lot of the problems, but provided sufficient answers to allow a very loose set of tender documents to be prepared. As engineers we floundered behind, realising that this making process had been much more useful than our calculations. In addition, we had neither the time nor the money to try to make an accurate computer model of a geometry that was still evolving. We knew enough to say that 4mm ply sheets were not strong enough and to worry that the whole thing might take off like a box-

The completed pavilion outside the Royal Festival Hall in the summer of 2009.

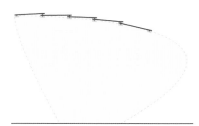

Urban Salon's section through the pavilion indicating how the poly-carbonate sheets might be overlapped to create a waterproof cover.

The initial concept called for a flexible timber lattice, assembled flat on the ground and then folded into its final shape. The lattice would be fixed down by stacks of paving slabs that would double as seating and temporary ballast.

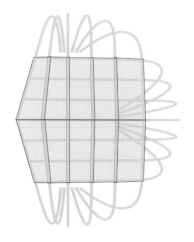

Urban Salon's plan with the number of polycarbonate sheets a careful balance between providing protection from the weather while minimising wind loads.

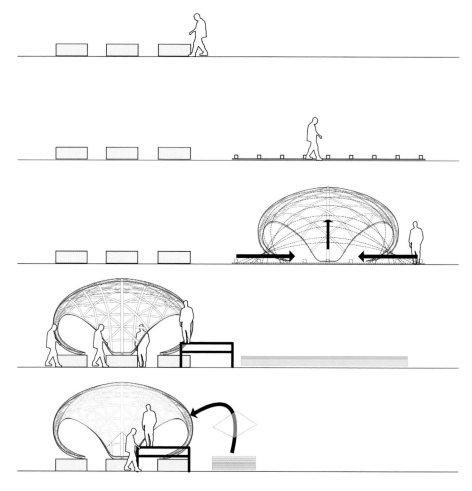

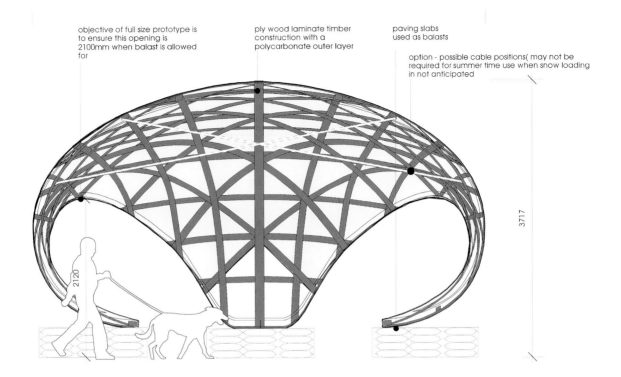

objective of full size prototype is to ensure this opening is 2100mm when balast is allowed for

ply wood laminate timber construction with a polycarbonate outer layer

paving slabs used as balasts

option - possible cable positions(may not be required for summer time use when snow loading in not anticipated

3717

2120

objective of full size prototype is to ensure this opening is 2100mm when balast is allowed for

ply wood laminate timber construction with a polycarbonate outer layer

paving slabs used as balast

In its final form, the structure of a flexible geogrid was superseded by the introduction of pre-curved plywood bands that would both hold their shape and be far stronger.

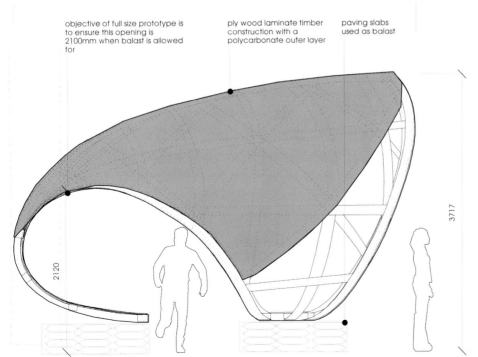

3717

2120

The final form of the pavilion was arranged to allow entry from both sides and the front.

Muttering, swearing, prodding and poking – but no computers – in Gordon Cowley's workshop!

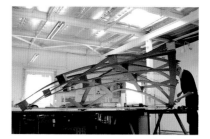

Urban Salon's early explorations with flexed plywood produced far shallower curves than achieved in the final design.

kite unless we found a way to anchor it down during its temporary residence on the concourse in front of the Royal Festival Hall.

Thankfully Gordon won the tender, which was a huge relief to Fluid and, almost certainly, to Alex as well. Gordon took the concept, nodded a few times, did a bit of muttering and set about building something in the spirit of the architect's requirements. The plywood bands turned into three sheets of best-grade 6mm plywood which he glued together in the required curved forms. Parallel bands were separated by timber blocks measuring approximately 100 x 100 x 100mm, bolted through to form what were 'almost' curved Vierendeel trusses – I say almost as the blocks weren't always glued. In this way, the ribbons – which were about 120 to 130mm wide and spaced at approximately 900mm centres – were able to span the seven-metre width of the pavilion and support the transparent blue plastic cladding material. I gave the bands a good shake in the workshop to get a feel for the strength and, while I wouldn't claim that the system could support a snow load of 80kg/m^2 in the long term, the solution was certainly strong enough to survive the pavilion's anticipated short summer lifespan.

Detail showing the connection between the main double pre-curved plywood ribs, using a wood block as a spacer and a bolt.

The pod was partially pre-assembled in Gordon's workshop and then taken apart for transfer to site.

The scheme's success shows that as long as a project is set up in such a way that the contractor feels he has space to breathe and that his knowledge and contributions will be welcomed rather than stifled, building mock-ups and prototypes can often solve many problems. It would have taken us a month of Sundays to develop and analyse digital versions of the scheme and the fee expenditure would have been enormous.

As planned, the pavilion was assembled outside the Royal Festival Hall in the summer of 2009, where it served as a venue for the RIBA and BBC during the Thames Festival. It held up well to a large number of curious visitors and was dismantled that autumn.

Detail views of the pavilion showing the polycarbonate 'roof' and the careful arrangement of the spacing blocks.

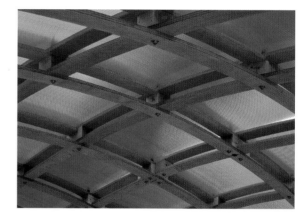

With the pre-assembly in Gordon's workshop having ironed out any problems, the erection of the main frame was completed in less than one day.

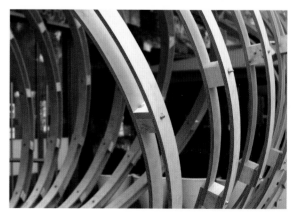

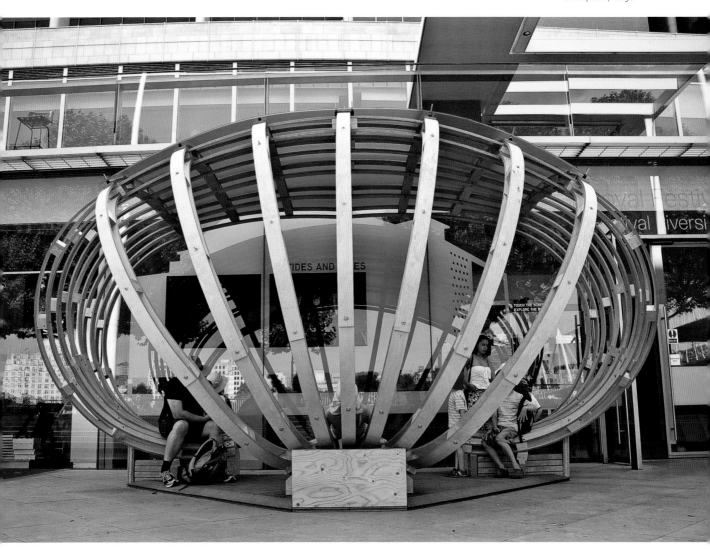

Nestling against the Royal Festival Hall, the pavilion was used throughout the summer as a quiet seating area, a meeting place and a temporary stage.

Lodona House

Lodona was a new-build house that came to us very early on. I think that it was possibly our second or third year in practice and, at the time, it was a considerable commission. The architect was Paul Bell, formerly of Terry Farrell's office, and he was committed to the design of a modern contemporary house. The client also took a very keen interest in the scheme's development and it soon became clear that what he wanted was a timber-framed home and that the common ground in the design existed around Frank Lloyd Wright's Prairie Houses.

The prospect of building a new two-storey, open-plan timber-framed house with lots of glazing was intriguing, but also a little worrying. Typically we would have proposed building in steel, which would have easily accommodated the open-plan living that the client envisaged. Timber framing, specifically in green oak, was more of a concern and we were apprehensive about its use in a contemporary space. Green oak is the name commonly given to wood which has a moisture content of 30 per cent or more, which means that it contains both bound water (within the cells) and free water (within the cavities). It's much cheaper to use than kiln-dried

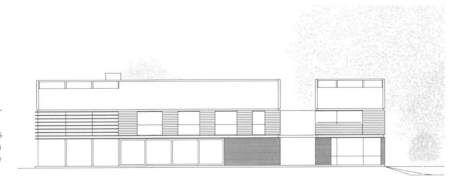

Architect Paul Bell's design elevation showing the glass link that acts as the main circulation area and stairwell for the new house.

oak, which has a moisture content of less than 18 per cent, but is prone to splitting and twisting as it naturally dries down to the moisture content of its surroundings. It's often used for barn-type buildings or recreating Tudor style homes but, to my knowledge, has rarely been used for contemporary dwellings.

We were also lost when it came to knowing how to make and conceal connections in a house that was to openly display its framing. Steel bolts could be used with angle plates but this type of solution seemed inappropriate for the material and for its usage in the client's home. After a period of research we began a dialogue with a number of specialist timber contractors who were experienced in working with the material. They all built green oak frames for houses, garages, outbuildings and so on, and tended to keep a handbook with several

The end elevation of the finished house looking into the double-height living area with its external deck and fixed timber louvres to provide shade from the sun.

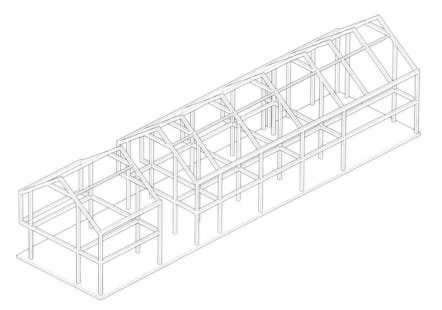

Isometric view showing the main elements of the timber structure, as produced by Heart of Oak.

variations that the client could choose from. We wanted their experience and input, but not their pre-packaged architectural solutions. Through these early conversations, we immersed ourselves in construction techniques that had developed over hundreds of years, eventually focusing on a very decent contractor, Heart of Oak, who guided us through the detailed use of tenon and mitred finger joints and the use of hardwood timber pegs to effect connections.

We, in turn, checked their sizes on our computer analysis packages, fretted about movement and sway, and slowly built up a better understanding of how the frame would perform. We learnt that you could build a modern house with green oak columns and beams in a primary framework, while using softwoods for the floor joists and wall studding. The house was sheathed against racking using plywood and oriented strand board (OSB), and I think there may even have been a couple of flitch beams (timber with a sandwiched steel plate) where the spans or loads got too tricky.

We also had to balance the language of contemporary architecture, shadow gaps and butt-jointed glass framing with a material that moves and, by its nature, will shrink and twist. Thus some of the more exacting details were designed out and junctions of dissimilar materials were allowed to breathe by designing in mullions and channels that would tolerate shrinkage and movement without cracking.

Lodona is a fine contemporary home and stands as a testament to the use of traditional materials in a new way. The project gave us confidence and showed us the importance of bringing on board experts who work with a material they love. The architect and design team may have pushed them beyond their normal comfort zone and held out for a house that had all the attributes of a contemporary design, but we could not have solved the design problems without their help. The techniques that inform this language of construction were not in our vocabulary as engineers.

One of the green oak trusses during erection on site, showing the timber dowels used to securely peg each joint.

The ground-floor plan, with the main living areas to one side of the house looking out over the garden, connected by an informal circulation area to the rear.

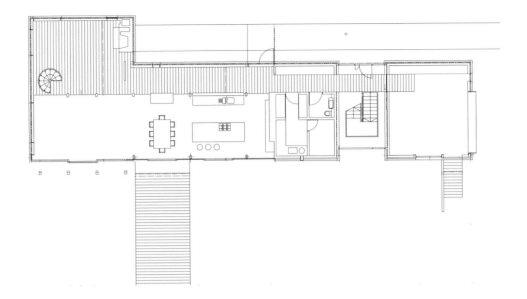

The first-floor plan follows the pattern of the floor below, with a circulation zone at the rear leading to the individual bedrooms and a small study that overlooks the main living area below.

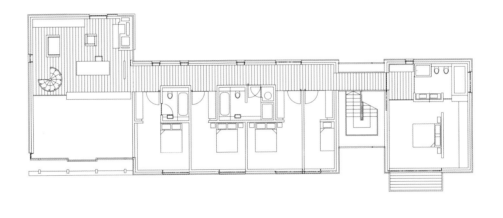

Two sections through the house showing the primary elements of the timber frame.

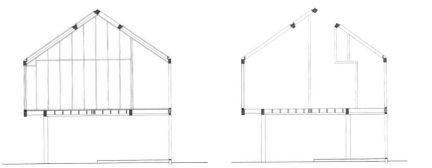

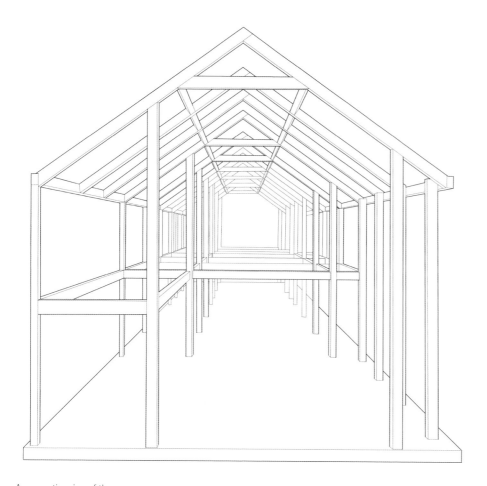

A perspective view of the main structural frame, with the double-height space of the main living area in the foreground.

A variety of green oak connections were used, including the joint between roof joist and eaves beam (1), a triple tenon connection (2), a secret mitred finger joint (3), and a double-sided T joint (4).

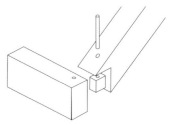

1

The house under construction with scaffold access to the eaves and roof, where fixing the secondary structure is under way.

Detail view of one of the main roof trusses, like the rest of the frame erected entirely without metal fixings.

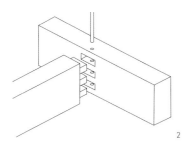

2

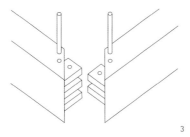

3

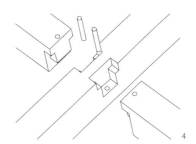

4

The internal walls are lined with oriented strand board (OSB) to provide racking resistance for the frame.

An end elevation of the
house as produced by
Paul Bell Architectural
Design.

The front or garden
elevation of the house
with its horizontal oak
boarding to the facade
beneath a slate tile roof.

An internal view of main
double-height living
area on the ground floor,
with the single-height
kitchen space beyond.

Longford Community School

I have known Jonathan Clark for a long time. He's a typical sole practitioner in his late 40s, a handsome Englishman who has made his name doing high-end residential work, restaurants and bars. He moved around a good deal when he was younger and has lots of funny stories about the famous architects he worked for.

When he first approached us about Longford Community School I was quite surprised to find him involved in this type of work. He had done some small fit-out work for the school and had come up with an interesting and successful storage system used by the kids. It's good that architects should cross over into different project types. Who's to say that the things you learn when you are working on bars and restaurants won't be useful when you're designing for schools? Our project involved extending the existing school building to provide ancillary space and a new library at first-floor level. Jonathan wanted the extension to be done in timber and this sat well with the school's environmental policy and their desire for the work to have a low carbon footprint.

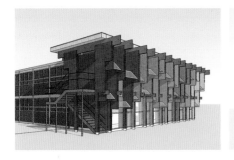 

Early computer drawings by Jonathan Clark Architects that explore the 'language' of the facade.

Jonathan Clark's school storage system, also for Longford School, that became a catalyst for the new elevation.

To support the new first floor and roof, the design called for external timber columns that would double as sunshades, which we decided could best be fabricated using Kerto laminated veneer lumber (LVL), a layered composite of wood veneers and adhesive. LVL was particularly attractive as it maintains the natural beauty of wood, is stronger than solid timber or glue laminated sections and is suitable for external use. Each column is made up of three layers, two outer fins that step out irregularly at the upper levels, while the intermediate layer stops short where necessary to allow the roof and floor beams to project through in a pronounced mortice and tenon joint. Solid timber roof beams at approximately two-metre centres are complemented by first-floor beams of flitch-plate construction, to provide the additional strength required to support the library.

Initial analysis showed that the individual timber fins could be 35mm thick, creating a 105mm-thick column that would be more than strong enough to support the roof and floor

The front elevation of the new extension, its structural narrative clearly expressed by the Kerto beam and coloured fin assembly.

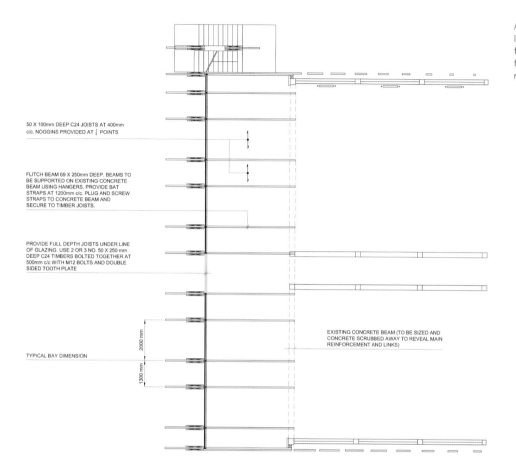

A structural plan of the library extension on the first floor, showing the flitch beams and external fin supports.

50 X 100mm DEEP C24 JOISTS AT 400mm c/c. NOGGINS PROVIDED AT $\frac{1}{3}$ POINTS

FLITCH BEAM 69 X 250mm DEEP. BEAMS TO BE SUPPORTED ON EXISTING CONCRETE BEAM USING HANGERS. PROVIDE BAT STRAPS AT 1200mm c/c. PLUG AND SCREW STRAPS TO CONCRETE BEAM AND SECURE TO TIMBER JOISTS.

PROVIDE FULL DEPTH JOISTS UNDER LINE OF GLAZING. USE 2 OR 3 NO. 50 X 250 mm DEEP C24 TIMBERS BOLTED TOGETHER AT 500mm c/c WITH M12 BOLTS AND DOUBLE SIDED TOOTH PLATE

2000 mm

1300 mm

TYPICAL BAY DIMENSION

EXISTING CONCRETE BEAM (TO BE SIZED AND CONCRETE SCRUBBED AWAY TO REVEAL MAIN REINFORCEMENT AND LINKS)

Model studies of the structure were prepared by Fluid Structures to explore various stability and assembly issues.

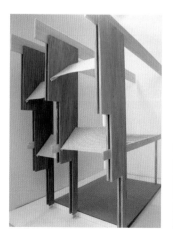

Matthew Turner of Fluid Structures with a sample of laminated veneer lumber (LVL).

A hand-drawn isometric showing the mortice and tenon-style connection details between the roof and floor beams and the LVL fin columns.

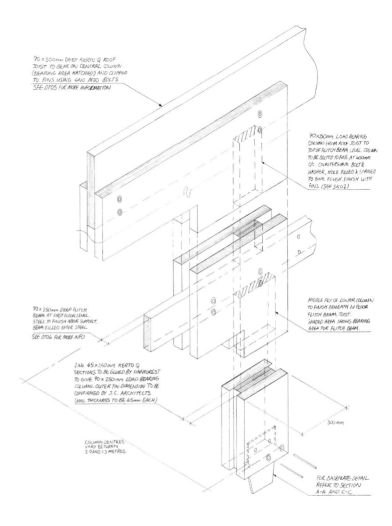

90 x 500mm DEEP KERTO Q ROOF
JOIST TO BEAR ON CENTRAL COLUMN
(BEARING AREA HATCHED) AND CLIPPED
TO FINS USING 4No. M20 BOLTS
SEE DT05 FOR MORE INFORMATION

90 x 250mm LOAD BEARING
COLUMN FROM ROOF JOIST TO
TOP OF FLITCH BEAM LEVEL. COLUMN
TO BE BOLTED TO FINS AT 400mm
C/C. COUNTERSUNK BOLT &
WASHER, HOLE FILLED & STAINED
TO GIVE FLUSH FINISH WITH
FINS (SEE SK02)

MIDDLE PLY OF LOWER COLUMN
TO FINISH BENEATH 1st FLOOR
FLITCH BEAM JOIST.
SHADED AREA SHOWS BEARING
AREA FOR FLITCH BEAM.

90 x 250mm DEEP FLITCH
BEAM AT FIRST FLOOR LEVEL.
STEEL TO FINISH ABOVE SUPPORT.
BEAM FILLED AFTER STEEL.
SEE DT06 FOR MORE INFO

2No. 45 x 250mm KERTO Q
SECTIONS TO BE GLUED BY FINNFOREST
TO GIVE 90 x 250mm LOAD BEARING
COLUMN. OUTER FIN DIMENSION TO BE
CONFIRMED BY J.C. ARCHITECTS
(MIN. THICKNESS TO BE 45mm EACH)

300 mm

COLUMN CENTRES
VARY BETWEEN
2.0 AND 13 METRES

FOR BASEPLATE DETAIL
REFER TO SECTION
A-A AND C-C

The side elevations of the existing classroom block showing the location and detailing of the new extension at one end.

A section through the
extension showing the
primary structural ele-
ments and the position
of the glazing relative to
the Kerto fins.

A detail of the column
support, the coloured LVL
fins raised above ground
level on short sections of
galvanised I beam.

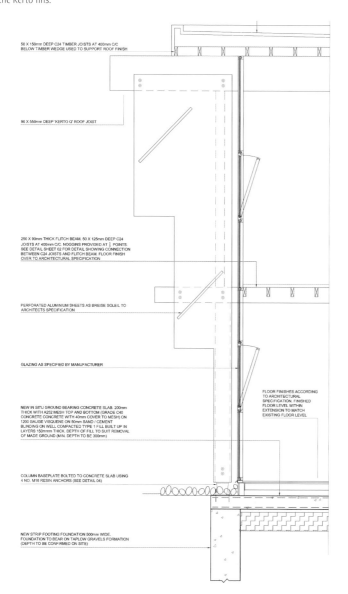

50 X 150mm DEEP C24 TIMBER JOISTS AT 400mm C/C
BELOW TIMBER WEDGE USED TO SUPPORT ROOF FINISH

90 X 550mm DEEP 'KERTO Q' ROOF JOIST

250 X 90mm THICK FLITCH BEAM. 50 X 125mm DEEP C24
JOISTS AT 400mm C/C. NOGGINS PROVIDED AT ⅓ POINTS.
SEE DETAIL SHEET 02 FOR DETAIL SHOWING CONNECTION
BETWEEN C24 JOISTS AND FLITCH BEAM. FLOOR FINISH
OVER TO ARCHITECTURAL SPECIFICATION

PERFORATED ALUMINIUM SHEETS AS BREISE SOLEIL TO
ARCHITECTS SPECIFICATION

GLAZING AS SPECIFIED BY MANUFACTURER

FLOOR FINISHES ACCORDING
TO ARCHITECTURAL
SPECIFICATION. FINISHED
FLOOR LEVEL WITHIN
EXTENSION TO MATCH
EXISTING FLOOR LEVEL

NEW IN SITU GROUND BEARING CONCRETE SLAB. 200mm
THICK WITH A252 MESH TOP AND BOTTOM (GRADE C40
CONCRETE CONCRETE WITH 40mm COVER TO MESH) ON
1200 GAUGE VISQUENE ON 50mm SAND / CEMENT
BLINDING ON WELL COMPACTED TYPE 1 FILL BUILT UP IN
LAYERS 150mm THICK. DEPTH OF FILL TO SUIT REMOVAL
OF MADE GROUND (MIN. DEPTH TO BE 300mm)

COLUMN BASEPLATE BOLTED TO CONCRETE SLAB USING
4 NO. M16 RESIN ANCHORS (SEE DETAIL 04)

NEW STRIP FOOTING FOUNDATION 500mm WIDE.
FOUNDATION TO BEAR ON TAPLOW GRAVELS FORMATION
(DEPTH TO BE CONFIRMED ON SITE)

A detail drawing of the
connection between the
I-beam support and fin
column, showing the I
beam partially concealed
below ground level.

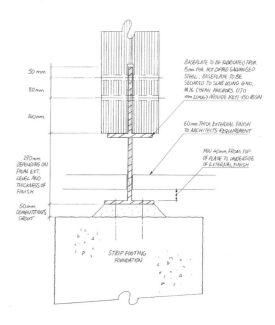

50 mm

80 mm

140 mm

290 mm
DEPENDING ON
FINAL EXT.
LEVEL AND
THICKNESS OF
FINISH

50 mm
CEMENTITIOUS
GROUT

BASEPLATE TO BE FABRICATED FROM
15mm THK. HOT DIPPED GALVANISED
STEEL. BASEPLATE TO BE
SECURED TO SLAB USING 4 NO.
M 16 CHEMI ANCHORS (170
mm LONG) PROVIDE HILTI ·150 RESIN

60mm THICK EXTERNAL FINISH
TO ARCHITECTS REQUIREMENT

MIN 40mm FROM TOP
OF PLATE TO UNDERSIDE
OF EXTERNAL FINISH

STRIP FOOTING
FOUNDATION

loads. However, to take account of fire issues and allow for the effect of charring, the fins needed to be increased to 90mm thick. As it happened, this worked out well as the increased timber thickness allowed Kerto to offer a greater lifespan than would have been achievable if the timber thicknesses were only provided sufficient strength to support the vertical loads.

The stepped out form provides solar shading to the south-facing facade, supplemented by sloping horizontal mesh shades that further enrich the elevation. The Kerto framing was prefabricated in Germany and arrived on site fully treated, with a specification that included an Adler impregnation against insect and fungus attack followed by two coats of Adler Pullex paint. Unlike traditional timber stains, the colours are strong and vibrant.

There had been a bit of a tussle between the German company's desire to do what they always do and Jonathan's need to design every detail and understand exactly how it would look prior to erection. This level of attention even crossed over into the specification of which fixings would be revealed, what type they would be, and what could and should be

The 13 preassembled LVL fin columns and roof beams that make up the extension's main structure were installed in just four days.

hidden. As Kerto is usually used in a structural context and hidden from view, this took longer than expected, but was essential in transferring the technology to its new more 'front of house' role. After some initial resistance, Kerto embraced this new approach and the frames were successfully signed off on schedule.

The Kerto components arrived on the key date at the beginning of the summer holidays and the whole structural frame – including the fin columns, first-floor beams and roof elements – was erected within four days, allowing all the major building work to be completed before the children returned for the autumn term, an important consideration from the school's point of view. The extension to Longford Community School was a modest project tackled in an inventive spirit with real collaboration between the design team. We were therefore delighted when Jonathan won an RIBA Award for the building in 2010.

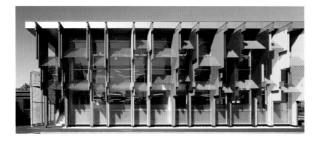

The front elevation of the new extension showing the coloured LVL fins and the angled galvanised mesh sunshades fixed between them.

An internal view of the first-floor extension to the library with the fins visible beyond the full-height glazing.

Children in the library extension, with its exposed roof beams and suspended light shades.

The new extension from the south-west, showing the new galvanised metal fire escape.

A close-up of the Kerto LVL fins showing their bolted connections to the projecting flitch beams that support the roof and first floor.

The angled mesh screens between the fins provide solar shading to this south-facing elevation.

An evening view of the extension with lights ablaze at both the lower classroom and upper library levels.

Huttons Farm

The timber and glass dome at Huttons Farm forms the centrepiece of a project that saw a very large Chiltern farm transformed into a new family home. This involved the restoration of listed barns and the construction of a new house, for which the dome and its timber-framed structure mark the main entrance. Associated engineering challenges included a large new basement – accommodating an underground art gallery – and a moat that partially surrounds and protects the overall complex. The scheme came to us via the project manager, Colm Morris, and our previous association with the architects, Giles Quarme and Associates. We have worked with Giles's practice on a number of occasions and each time the project has afforded us an opportunity to be involved in richly bespoke design work.

The dome's form is based on the Fibonacci sequence, where the number and position of the nodes is derived from a strict mathematical formula. This was important as it allowed for repetition in the detailing of the dome's geometry, which had a significant effect on the cost of manufacture. The dome also represents the culmination of current timber jointing

Giles Quarme's sketch of the main entry space beneath the dome, with its curved staircase.

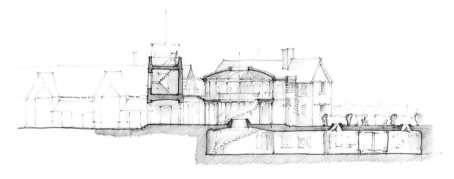

Giles Quarme's sketch section showing the position of the dome in the context of the new farmhouse building and refurbished barns.

techniques and is a showpiece for contemporary timber skills. It is heir to the great medieval tithe-barns with their green oak cruck frames, and to hammer-beam and king-post roofs. Julian Cripps, the project architect, came up with the sunflower geometry and the idea of a timber lineage, and we're pretty certain this helped them to win the project.

The scheme was considerably enriched by the participation of Gordon Cowley, who is without doubt the finest timber designer and sometime contractor in the country. Prior to this project we knew of him only by reputation and his involvement in some of the finest timber projects in the UK. Gordon was the contractor for the roof of the Scottish Parliament building, designed by Enric Miralles, as well as the double-curved plywood pods at Will Alsop's Peckham Library. He is also the proud designer of a timber joint known as the Cowley

The finished dome floods the entrance space with light during the day, with illumination at night provided by a purpose-designed chandelier.

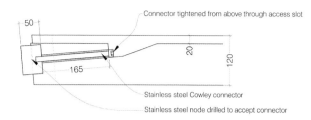

50

165

20

120

Connector tightened from above through access slot

Stainless steel Cowley connector

Stainless steel node drilled to accept connector

Section showing how the connecting rod is fitted to the central steel node via a concealed slot cut into the top of the timber strut.

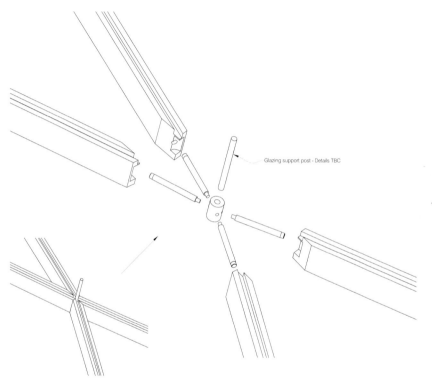

Glazing support post - Details TBC

An exploded drawing showing how the metal rods and central node of the Cowley Connector are completely hidden in the finished joint.

The exact layout of the dome's timber elements follows the Fibonacci mathematical sequence by which, for example, sunflower seeds are also arranged in nature.

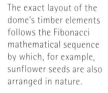

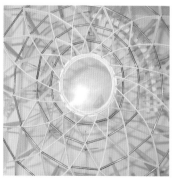

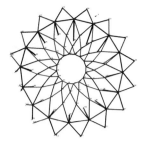

A variety of computer models were generated by Fluid Structures to analyse the stresses in the dome and thus determine the correct sizes for the different elements.

The dome's geometry follows a clear pattern, with an equal number of nodes in each ring and the length of the timber elements at each stage established by the Fibonacci sequence.

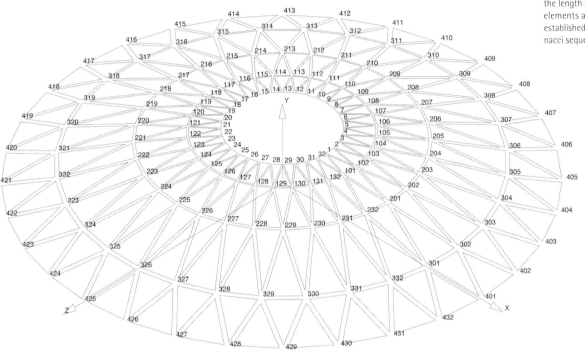

The mixture of card, steel wire and balsa wood may be crude, but this model allowed Fluid Structures to fully explore the geometry of the dome and develop a better understanding of its structure.

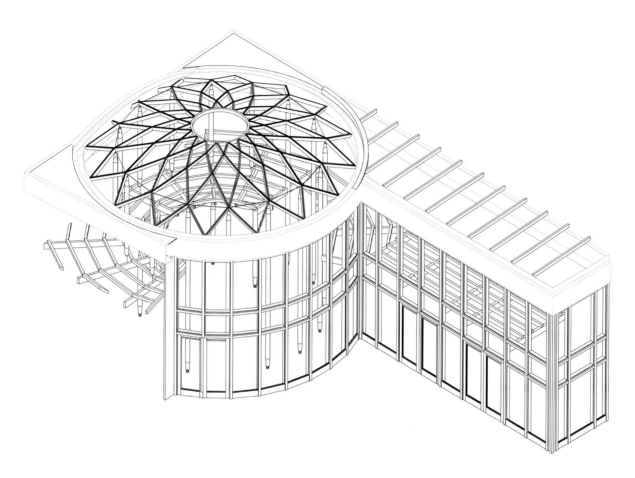

A drawing prepared by Gordon Cowley's team, showing all the timber elements required to complete the new entrance.

The entrance atrium and central dome roof under construction.

Connector, which allows a number of timber elements converging at a single point to be secured in a structurally sound but architecturally satisfactory method.

The dome – which is approximately 10 metres in diameter – is supported on slender oak columns topped by stainless-steel cones that facilitate their connection to the dome, which is made up of 60 x 120mm American white oak elements joined by the aforementioned connector. The dome was analysed and sized using computer software that considered various conditions, including wind loading and the asymmetrical loads due to drifting snow. Consideration was also given at an early stage to the support of the glass cladding, which was to be propped off the dome's nodes on bespoke bronze connectors. Laminated glass was preferred to double glazing as this would avoid the individual facets being outlined by unacceptably intrusive lines of black structural silicone.

Computer modelling by the environmental engineers showed that this would be acceptable, not least because double-glazed units were likely to exacerbate the possibility of

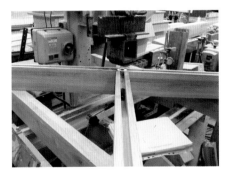  

The strength of the specified connector was tested in Gordon's workshop *(above)*, prior to the dome's erection on site *(above right)*.

the space beneath the dome becoming a heat sink. The dome was therefore designed to support laminated toughened glass units which, due to their shallower depth, could be sealed using clear weatherproof silicone. The dome's structure was prefabricated by Gordon's firm at his workshop in Lincoln and then pre-assembled to verify its structural performance and to confirm that it could be erected within the tight tolerances required when inserted into the pre-built entrance courtyard.

Due to changes in the design team, the main contractor was tasked with procuring the glass package and its associated support fixings on a design-and-build basis, which led to the bespoke fixings and their specific locations being lost – although the laminated glass and clear structural silicone remained. It is safe to say that the fixings installed would have benefited greatly from the original design team's involvement as, in this case, less would

One of Giles Quarme's competition-winning sketches, showing the collection of buildings that form the whole farmhouse complex.

certainly have been more. However, this does not take away from the magnificence of the original architectural idea and the pleasure in seeing something of this grandeur, through from its conception on paper to fruition.

The timberwork of the dome roof at Huttons Farm is testimony to the great craftsmanship involved, which is itself the result of Gordon's determination to carry out all his projects to the highest standard. As engineers, we are blessed to meet people like him, and engineers, architects, indeed any sort of designer should seize every opportunity to draw on the vast amount of knowledge and refinement that lies with such specialist manufacturers and contractors.

A view of the house as it nears completion, showing the dome and its surrounding glazed entrance atrium.

An overview of the new farmhouse and its protective moat, showing how the entrance atrium and dome forms the central connection between the two wings.

A view of one of the existing barns, all of which were extensively refurbished during the building process.

An internal view of the upper level of the entrance atrium, showing the stainless-steel connections between the tops of the oak 'cigar' columns and the dome.

Looking up from the ground floor towards the dome's American white oak structure and the laminated glass skin, the latter notable for its clear rather than black silicone joints.

A view of the curved stair that leads up to the first floor, complete with oak treads, steel strings and a cantilevered glass balustrade.

A detail drawing of one of the laminated oak 'cigar' columns showing its stainless-steel head and base plate connections.

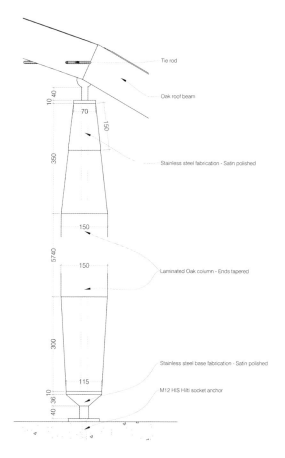

Tie rod

Oak roof beam

Stainless steel fabrication - Satin polished

Laminated Oak column - Ends tapered

Stainless steel base fabrication - Satin polished

M12 HIS Hilti socket anchor

10
40
70
150
350
150
150
5740
300
115
40
36
10

Archway Early Years Centre

A diagrammatic elevation of the new two-storey extension to the existing single-storey nursery.

In the summer of 2004, we were approached by the German architect Kay Hartmann, who lives and practises in London. He needed our help with two projects for Islington Council's Early Years Education Department. The first, Hargrave Park School, was the simple refurbishment of a four-storey Victorian brick building that required some new openings at ground-floor level. In contrast, the second – for the Archway Early Years Centre – involved the construction of a new two-storey block adjacent to the existing centre, then housed in a single-storey brick building. The Hargrave Park School work proved pretty normal, but the AEYC scheme was the start of our involvement with cross-laminated timber construction and its use in the UK.

The scheme required the creation of a new creative environment for the children's centre, which evolved conceptually by adapting the two-storey form specified in the brief to better acknowledge the context of the site. The design proposed a series of interconnecting spaces which varied in width and height. Courtyards, entrances and through routes were created that responded to the rooms' specific internal requirements as well as their relationship to the centre's existing external spaces.

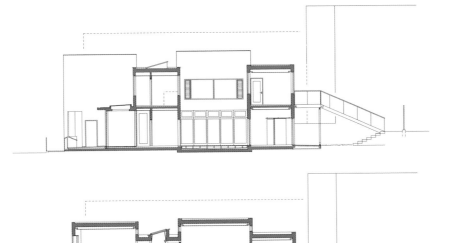

A cross-section through the new entrance and internal courtyard of the extension, next to the existing nursery.

A cross-section through the main part of the extension, with a parents' room, training area and crèche at ground level, and new staff facilities on the floor above.

226   TIMBER

The garden elevation looking into the new crèche on the ground floor and the staff room above, with its galvanised metal balcony.

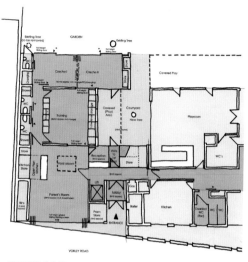

GROUND FLOOR

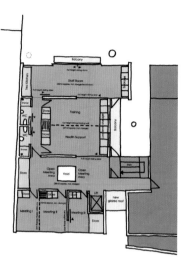

FIRST FLOOR

Sketch plans of the two-storey extension, with the new entrance area (shown in red) providing the link between the existing playrooms and new teaching areas on the ground floor, with the first floor reserved for the staff.

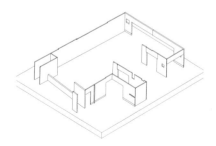

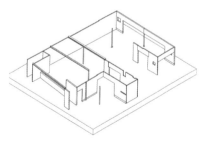

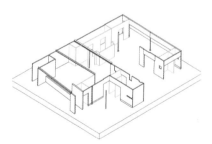

KLH Massivholz's 10-stage construction sequence for the cross-laminated timber superstructure.

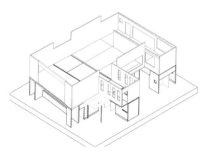

KLH Massivholz's sketch section, showing the main features
of the building's construction, including:

1 **roof build up**, with a waterproof membrane laid over insulation to
  falls and a vapour barrier on the laminated timber roof element,
  finished with an insulated suspended plasterboard ceiling below

2 **external wall build up**, with a painted insulated render system over
  a vapour barrier on the laminated timber wall element, with a plasterboard inner lining and mdf skirting boards

5 **first-floor build up**, with a factory finished, floating timber floor over
  underlay, a non-screed type underfloor heating system and impact
  sound insulation and a balast layer on the laminated timber floor
  element with a suspended plasterboard ceiling with insulation below

9 recessed luminaire

11 aluminium capping, polyester powder coated to RAL colour

12 painted suspended plasterboard ceiling with insulation

13 **ground-floor build up**, with the chosen floor covering over a separation layer, screed replacement tiles, a non-screed type underfloor
  heating system, thermal insulation and a damp-proof membrane on
  a reinforced concrete slab and pile foundations to engineer's details

21 **internal wall build up**, with a painted plasterboard lining and mdf
  skirting boards to both sides of the laminated timber wall element

26 existing masonry wall with a plastered inner face

39 floating screed finish

40 painted WBP ply over thermal insulation and a vapour barrier on a
  laminated timber wall element with a plasterboard inner lining

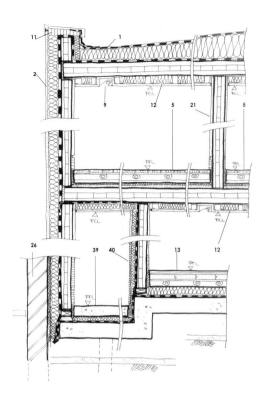

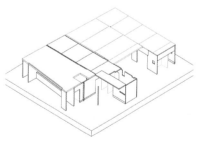

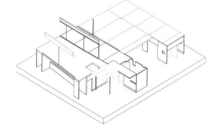

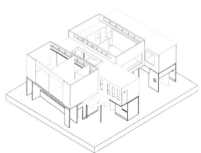

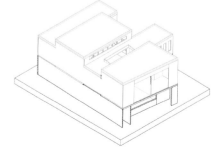

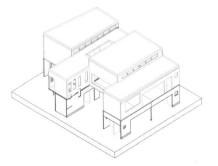

Ralph Swallow of Fluid
Structures holding a
sample piece of cross-
laminated timber.

Funding was tight for a building with a gross floor area of some 360 square metres and things were not helped by the ground conditions. Site investigations had revealed that beneath a metre or so of fill there was good London Clay, but there were also several mature London plane trees in the vicinity that were likely to cause the soil to dry out and shrink. The foundations would therefore need to be piled and the ground slab suspended, a solution that significantly ate into the cost plan and made it essential that the superstructure was built as economically as possible.

The architect drove the scheme forward and asked for alternative structural solutions. We came up with a steel-frame scheme first, followed by one made up of timber floor joists on timber stud walls, with a few bits of steelwork straddling the bigger spans. Kay preferred the timber option but, because of his German background, thought it could be improved with the use of cross-laminated timber. He introduced us to KLH Massivholz, a young and dynamic timber company based in Murau, southern Austria, which produced units consisting of dried

The building arrived as a
'flat pack' on the back of
three lorries from Austria,
from where the various
elements were unloaded
directly on to site.

spruce boards, stacked and glued at right angles to each other, that seemed particularly suitable. They had not worked on a scheme in the UK before, but were up for the challenge.

One of the many advantages of this particular system is that the crossway arrangement of the lamellas reduces swelling and shrinkage to a minimum, making the boards very stable and suitable for prefabrication. Putting our heads together, we began to envisage a scheme where the concrete substructure would be topped by a superstructure made up exclusively of prefabricated wall, floor and roof panels. Excluding insulation and cladding, these could be erected in less than four weeks, which suited the tight programme and simplified some of the main contractor's other works.

The design consultants were quickly enamoured of the cross-laminated timber scheme, with its off-site construction and environmentally friendly low-carbon agenda, but the client

The prefabrication of the entire building combined with well organised logistics reduced erection time of the LVL superstructure to just 10 working days.

Due to site constraints, the cross-laminated timber panels had to be lifted on to site in the right order, directly to the locations where they belonged.

needed proof that the structural and architectural advantages would stand up to financial scrutiny. In early 2005, Colin Hayward of the cost consultants KMCS completed an appraisal which reported that a steel-framed option would result in a higher overall cost than the partly prefabricated KLH option. It also compared favourably with similar solutions by other suppliers, both domestic and international. The report concluded that there would be no problem asking KLH to act as a domestic subcontractor.

With the prefabricated panel scheme fully vindicated, any concerns the client might have had regarding the competitiveness of the price or the contractual precedents were allayed and approval quickly followed. The scheme proceeded to site with KLH responsible for the design, fabrication and erection of the superstructure, the last phase of which was completed in just 10 working days under the auspices of the main contractor.

Cross-laminated timber panel systems have proved to be a successful timber solution in the last half decade and, since this first small project, the material has been used for a vast

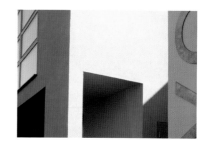

A facade detail of the insulated render system.

The full depth of the first floor, from the open meeting area to the staff room *(far left)*, and the ground-floor parents' room looking through to the internal courtyard *(left)*, showing how the sliding walls allow maximum flexibility.

array of schools, private residences, churches, theatres and art installations throughout the UK. The advantages of prefabrication and its ease of erection, coupled with its sustainability credentials, make it an attractive way to approach compartmentalised buildings. More importantly, building with panels just seems a sensible thing to do, especially when the panels can be cut, routed, recessed and manipulated to suit the whims of the most demanding designer.

Note: I should mention that Matthew Wells' office, Techniker, helped KLH develop their connection detailing to meet British Standards. It was the start of a fruitful relationship that has since developed considerably, culminating in their recent design for a nine-storey residential block using the same system.

Fully retractable folding doors facilitate the extension of the ground-floor training area into the courtyard, which also acts as the focus point for outdoor life at the new centre.

Cumnor House School

The Cumnor House School project involved the construction of a new two-storey building for an existing prep school on the edge of Ashdown Forest in Sussex. The architects, Marcus Beale Architects, were tasked with providing approximately 360 square metres of space to accommodate new classrooms and a design and technology teaching facility on a site then occupied by some dilapidated buildings. These were to be demolished to create an available ground-floor area measuring approximately 32 metres x 6.4 metres.

The key issue in the project was the client's requirement to develop the new building for an extremely challenging £1000/m², or as near as damn it! We got off to a good start when the site investigation showed that, below approximately a metre of clay and part fill, there was good ground. This meant that the new building could be constructed using concrete strip footings rather than other more costly solutions. The only bad news was that the top metre of clay was prone to drying out, meaning that the ground slab would have to be suspended. This is one step up from a ground-bearing slab in cost terms, but was easily resolved by specifying the use of Milbank precast concrete beams with block infill.

The superstructure proved more challenging, as the original cost plans prepared by

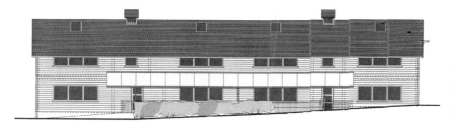

Marcus Beale Architects' drawing of the east elevation, which looks out over the school's inner courtyard.

the cost consultants, Pierce Hill, showed that the building was costing in the region of £1200 per square metre, with some £180,000 of that associated with the superstructure. Early on, when it became clear that costs were a problem, it was decided to bring in a timber contractor and to work with them to drive down the costs of the superstructure's most expensive component, the frame. Covers Timber Structures of Chichester were brought in to work with the design team and quantity surveyor to try to find a way of meeting the client's requirements in terms of both architectural brief and cost.

This approach worked very well: the timber contractor was able to identify the parts he could fabricate and supply cost effectively, while being similarly straightforward in pointing out which elements would be expensive if made in timber. The scheme therefore became a hybrid, with steel beams being introduced where there were heavy loads, or where timber beams would have compromised the floor to ceiling heights or had a significant effect on costs. The scheme

Looking along the east elevation showing the covered walkway and the external, shiplapped weatherboard cladding of untreated larch.

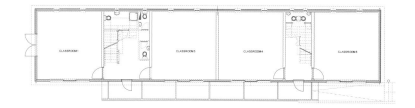

The ground-floor plan could hardly be simpler, consisting of four classrooms accessed via two entrances that also double as stairwells.

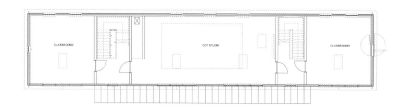

The first-floor plan is even simpler, with classrooms at either end and just a large workshop in the middle between the two staircases.

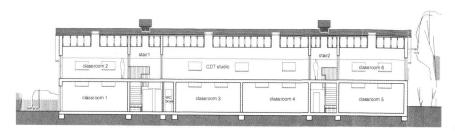

A long section through the building showing the allocation of spaces and the building's relatively simple internal structure.

developed with timber floors, walls and roof, but with steel beams along the central spine supported off blockwork cross walls around the staircases and elsewhere as necessary.

As a result of the contractor's involvement, the costs involved in the design and construction of the timber frame elements were halved from £42,000 to £21,000. A good example of this cost engineering was the change in the roof structure from glue-laminated timber portal frames to much simpler – and cheaper – timber scissor trusses, made up with softwood sections fixed together with common metalwork and sheathed in oriented strand board (OSB). Covers' commercial experience was essential in these decisions, as structural engineers are not always au fait in developing designs that meet specific architectural and engineering criteria, while also generating the easiest form to maximise economy.

The construction was carried out in spring 2006, with the timber frame erected in a period of just two weeks. The external walls consisted of 38mm x 90mm timber studs at 600mm centres, lined internally with plasterboard and backed with rigid insulation, and clad externally with horizontal timber boards fixed back to vertical battens. This hybrid or combination system might be considered an 'impure' response in that it involved two or three materials, but it remains a low technology approach. Indeed, in that each material is used to best advantage, it could also be described as a sophisticated solution. Whatever one's decision, the structural frame was brought in on budget and a small but charming building that had initially seemed impossible was achieved.

An early architectural model exploring the building's relationship with the rest of the school and the site.

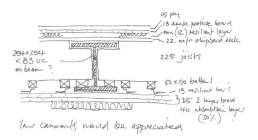

1. TIMBER CLADDING
2. 25×38mm VERTICAL BATTENS
3. TYVEK BREATHER MEMBRANE
4. 9.5mm OSB BOARD
5. 90×38mm STUDS
6. INSULATION
7. RESILIENT BARS
8. 18mm PLANK
9. 12.5mm PLASTERBOARD
10. 90×38 mm STUDS OFFSET ON 140mm SOLEPLATE
11. TYVEK VAPOUR CONTROL LAYER

← A275

Two architects' sketches detailing their thoughts on how the building's external walls and floors were to be constructed, including the concealed steel I-beam that helps support the first floor.

Fluid Structures prepared a variety of alternative sketch schemes to help identify the best structure in terms of matching the needs of both the timber contractor and the cost consultants.

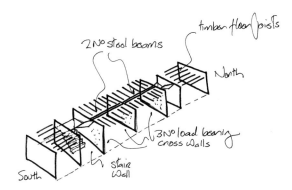

15 ply
13 dense particle board
thin (12.) resilient layer
22 m/r chipboard deck

294×254
×89 UC
so beam?

225 joists

50×50 batten!
19 resilient bar!
25 2 layer board.
40 absorbtion layer
(50%.)

your comments would be appreciated

A view of the finished building showing the traditional hand-made clay tiles as supplied by Keymer Tiles, a local manufacturer.

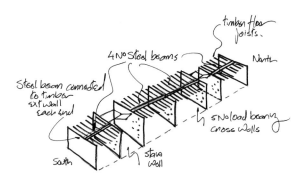

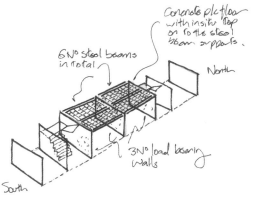

The south elevation opens on to a small terrace that incorporates an external chess board.

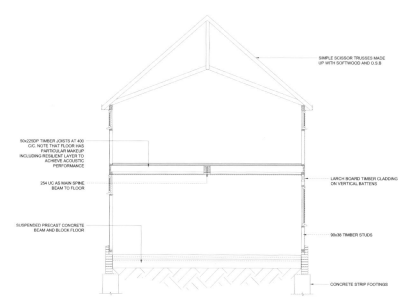

SIMPLE SCISSOR TRUSSES MADE UP WITH SOFTWOOD AND O.S.B

50x225DP TIMBER JOISTS AT 400 C/C. NOTE THAT FLOOR HAS PARTICULAR MAKEUP INCLUDING RESILIENT LAYER TO ACHIEVE ACOUSTIC PERFORMANCE

LARCH BOARD TIMBER CLADDING ON VERTICAL BATTENS

254 UC AS MAIN SPINE BEAM TO FLOOR

SUSPENDED PRECAST CONCRETE BEAM AND BLOCK FLOOR

90x38 TIMBER STUDS

CONCRETE STRIP FOOTINGS

A section through the building indicating the the I-beam that supports the centre of the first floor and the final form of the OSB-lined scissor trusses.

The building's barn-like form, as seen here from across the fields to the west, is subverted by the regular rhythm of the numerous small windows.

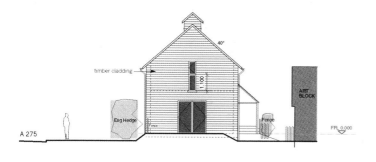

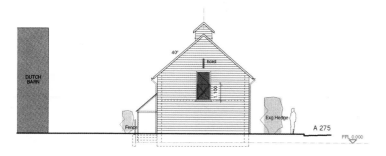

Marcus Beale's drawings of the building's south and north elevations, showing the full-height windows on the first floor to provide better light and views.

The finished building from the north-east, with the rooftop lanterns marking out the position of the internal stairwells.

Appendices

The Office

I would like to extend my thanks to my friend, colleague and business partner John Graham, the best engineer I ever met.

I would also like to thank the following people: Rachel Sandbrook, for her brains, humour and emotional support; Ralph Swallow, for his calmness, clear-headedness and independence; and Deirdre Gilbert, for her dedication to this book and her Irish charm. Finally, a thank you to Kevin Rowbotham for his friendship and intelligence over the years. Do not go quietly Kevin.

Staff List 2000-2010

Idil Abdulrahman
Joyce Adetoye
Francisco Alcazar
Innocentia Amegah
Hollie Barker
Alala Bitsat
Eric Boady
Kevin Boylan
Stuart Browne
Martin Byrne
Giorgio Cardone
Catherine Carpenter
Mandhir Chaggar
Kristina H. Chaung
Ieronymos Chochlakas
Mel Clarke
Kevin Coffey
Peter Cook
David Crookes
Andrew Crowley
Kerry Daly
Raquel Diaz
Henry Draper
Irina Dubroivina
Serome Efue
S. el Sayed
Marcos Fernandez
Isabel Flores

Himanshu Garg
Simon Garlick
Justine Garrel
Deirdre Gilbert
Klaus Gotthardt
John Graham
Richard Hardy
Timothy Harford-Cross
Steve Hastings
Raphaelle Heaf
Manhal Ibrahim
Amaka Iloduba
Zaneta Jiroutova
Ephraim O. Johny
Elani Kapsali
Dominata Kargbo
Marcin Kozlowski
Karina Krause
Helen Lamps
Nathan Langdon
Calvin Law
Heba Layas
Laure le Corre
Maria Lees
Patrick Lim
Giuseppe Loporcaro
Paul McIntyre
Guilleme Messina
Hash Mistry
Alison Morris
Geoff Morrow
Anthony Mulloy
Nirmal Nandara
Juri Nishi
Hedi Ollivier
Hargord Othman

Susan Ajibola Oyedele
Kim Peterson
Stefan Piasecki
Anjum Riaz
Tom Roberts
Karen Rogers
Joanne Saad
Rachel Sandbrook
David Scott
Hanna Shaw
Grace Simmonds
Divena Sinclair
Pornthina Sirirattana-Amporn
Kevin Smyth
Ayo Stubbs
Ralph Swallow
Michael Tan
Matthew Turner
Ahmet Ucakan
Farooq Waheed
Dylan Wright
Peter Yip
Marta Zadrozna

Consultants and Contractors

Special thanks to the following contractors, fabricators and makers, who really helped us along the way.

Contractors

John Evans at **Ash Construction**

David Osbourne at **Cosmo**
www.cosmogroup.co.uk

Joe Halpin at **Ellmer Construction**
www.ellmers.co.uk

Peter Pond and family at **Faberdex**

Colin and Neil at **Harris Calnan**
www.harriscalnan.co.uk

David Hobson at **John C. Lillywhite Ltd**
www.johnclillywhite.co.uk

Nick Melberg at Noil Connective

Gerry Vaughan at **Shannon Contracts**

Aluminium

Alan and James at **Barron Clark Castings**
www.barronclark-castings.co.uk

Glass

Malcolm Armfield at **Armfield Glass**
www.armfield.com

Mark and Johnny at **F.A. Firman**
www.firmanglass.com

Warren Evans at **Glass UK**
www.glass-uk.com

Ken Branscombe at **Solaglas**
www.Solaglas.co.uk

Walter Luessi at **Tuchschmid AG**
www.tuchschmid.ch

Masonry

Harrie Vekemans at **Adviesbureau Vekemans**
www.vekemans.nl

Paul Rogatzki at **Hanson Building Systems**
www.heidelbergcement.com/uk/en/hanson

Steel

Tony Culmer at **Culmax**
www.culmax.co.uk

Bill Tustin at **Littlehampton Welding**
www.littlehamptonwelding.co.uk

Mark Winder at **Silverfern Fabrications**
admin@silverfernltd.com

Timber

Gordon Cowley at **Cowley Timberwork**
www.cowleytimberwork.co.uk

Craig and Karl at **KLH UK**
www.klhuk.com

Credits

Fluid Structures

21 St George's Road
London SE1 6ES

tel   020 7820 7766
fax   020 7582 7848
david@fluidstructures.com

www.fluidstructures.com

*All photographs and drawings by
Fluid Structures, except as noted
to the right.*